D1242712

ANDERS
CD-ROM Survey

1996 edition

Richard and Judy Anders, publishers

Edited by Chris Shipley

Andiron Press, Inc.
Brookline, MA

Publishers: **Richard and Judy Anders,**
Andiron Press, Inc.

Editor: **Chris Shipley**

Business Advisor: **Herb Schnall**

Book Advisor: **Bob Diforio**

Project Manager: **John Swanson**

Children's Editor: **Warren Buckleitner**

Games Editor: **Paul Hyman**

Sports Games Editor: **Mark Cohen**

Senior Writer: **Vladimir Edelman**

Writers: **Emily Field, Ann Ritchie, Emily Kay**

Designer: **Meral Dabcovich, Visual Perspectives**

Database Consultant: **Jascha Franklin-Hodge**

Quark Production Consultant: **Cliff Garber**

In-house testing consultants:
Sarah Anders, Rebecca Anders

On-line pollster: **David Sheldon**

Copy Editor: **Phyllis Weinberg**

Printed in the United States of America

ISBN 1-888056-00-2

ACKNOWLEDGEMENTS

We have depended on the kindness of strangers, and friends, more than we ever expected. To everyone who helped us, even if we inadvertently left them from this page, we dedicate this book.

Michael Wolff for tremendous advice. Jonathan Adams, who helped teach us how to ask; Michael Sullivan, and Sara Bertacchi who designed the way for us to ask. Joe Mayr, who wields a mean, and fast, pencil. Pat Brown, Marty Grosjean, Maura Duncan, Cybersmith, The Computer Museum, Kathy McIlvane, Kathleen Baum, John Merson, Ralph Gilson, MicroCenter-Cambridge, Lana Lee and Egghead, Brookline, for making it possible for us to ask.The Boston Museum of Science Computer Discovery Space, Joanne Robinson's after-school class at Devotion School, Jane Manzelli, the Staff of Egghead Cambridge, and Cybersmith, for their opinions. Vadim Yasinofsky and Diane Franklin for advice and ideas. Doug Goewey of Paperback Booksmith and Randy Green of Greentree Associates, both for help in a pinch.

Sincere thanks to Judy Dunbar for her tireless help, and a special thanks to Steven Cipriano and Pat Collins. Adam Green for Web expertise and assistance. Mark Beldon for early assistance.

The underappreciated PR contacts at every multimedia company we worked with, who supported us in a million ways, culminating in rapid responses to our frantic phone calls near deadline.

George Meier Inc. and PC Data both diligently track the CD-ROM marketplace, and provide remarkably detailed statistics on CD-ROM sales by dollar volume and/or units. We have used data generously provided by both these organizations, to our great benefit.

George Meier Inc. can be reached at:
(201) 376-8181.
PC Data can be reached at:
(703) 435-1025

TABLE OF CONTENTS

About the Editors   VI

Introduction   VII

Foreword   VIII

The 99 Products
Rated Over 20   10

Key to Ratings and Symbols   12

Alphabetical Reviews
of Products   15

List of Companies with
Products in the Book   180

Title Locator with
products sorted by subject   195

ABOUT THE EDITORS

Chris Shipley is a long-time editor for Ziff-Davis Publishing Company and is currently responsible for online publishing projects at ComputerLife magazine. She writes a weekly column about CD-ROMs which is distributed by the New York Times Syndicate.

Warren Buckleitner is well-known as an expert in children's educational software. He is editor of the Children's Software Revue and a frequent contributor to HomePC magazine. He has won the prestigious Cody Award for best Computer Journalist, given by the Software Publisher's Association.

Mark Cohen, a professional sportswriter, is founding editor of PC Sports and Videogames, a magazine with a circulation of over 100,000. He co-hosts the nationally syndicated radio show PC Sports and Videogames Hour, which reaches over 200 markets. He will also be the host for an upcoming TV series about PC sports games.

Paul Hyman has been editing and writing about electronics and computers for more than 24 years. Paul writes articles about computer games regularly in more than a dozen publications, including Computer Shopper, Electronic Entertainment and Windows Magazine. He also reviews games for Delphi Internet, where he heads up the software forum. He helped launch the Electronic Buyers' News, where he was editor-in-chief for eight years. He's still trying to find enough time to tackle the long levels in Dark Forces.

Our guide is called a survey, because our approach is to evaluate CD-ROMs by surveying a broad base of opinions. Most CD-ROMs in our guide have been discussed by many people in many places: professional computer journalists write about them in computer magazines; end-users discuss them in on-line forums; they are reviewed in newspapers and even discussed in coffee shops.

Over the past year we have sent our Anders Questionnaire to well over 10,000 CD-ROM consumers. Our database system tracks the responses to these surveys as well as product reviews in all the leading publications. We've also gone online, ferreting out requests for user opinions and scrutinizing discussion groups in search of CD-ROM related information. The results of these forays are also included in our database. We believe all this information added together gives us a uniquely broad view of the products in the marketplace.

We are great fans of multimedia technology, and we have tremendous respect and appreciation for creators who commit years of effort and small fortunes to produce software. We are very excited by the great number of marvelous products we have found out there. Even so, not every disc is wonderful and even superb titles are not appropriate for every person. Our goal is to give you enough information to help you quickly decide whether a CD-ROM is right for you. We wanted our reviews to be short, easy-to-understand and fun-to-read. We wanted you to spend more time looking at multimedia titles and less time reading about them.

Buying a CD-ROM is more than a purchase, it's a commitment. A commitment to install it, to learn it, to teach it to your children. If you find this book helps you find interesting, useful and exciting CD-ROMs that suit your particular needs and desires, then we will have succeeded. Good luck, and enjoy your multimedia adventures!

If you want to fill out our survey and share your opinions of CD-ROMs with others, please send a self-addressed stamped envelope to:

Andiron Press Survey
PO Box 1600
Brookline, MA 02146

Those who complete our survey by the next book deadline will receive a free copy of the next edition of the book.

If you want to participate in the survey by E-Mail, send an internet message to:

survey@Andiron.com
or examine our web-site at:
http://www.andiron.com.

Richard Anders, October 1995

The Confusing Market for CD-ROMs

One year ago, this Guide would not have been necessary. A handful of CD titles spotted the shelves of computer stores, and only a few of them were widely publicized. CD-ROM drives were an extra-cost option on most personal computers and the lack of really useful CD titles made the expense of an upgrade difficult to justify.

Then seemingly over night, the tide turned. Through the 1994 holiday selling season computer manufacturers began to include CD-ROM drives in PCs as standard equipment. In the last three months of 1994, nearly three-quarters of all high-powered multimedia PCs were sold to consumers for use in their homes.

And the flood of multimedia CD-ROM titles began. Some 2,000 or more CD-ROM titles will hit the market before this year comes to a close. They will be sold by mail order, at computer retailers, in record stores, book stores, office supply warehouses —we've even seen them in golf pro shops. But even the most avid computer enthusiast is likely to purchase no more than about 20 discs a year, and that's why this guide is so necessary now.

It's impossible for any one person to sort through this mountain of discs to find the handful that will do the job, whether it's entertain the family, teach the kids, or organize daily life. But Andiron Press has been working for more than a year, gathering user opinions, reading magazine and newspaper reviews, and trying hundreds of discs in order to collect a consensus view of the most useful and enjoyable titles available. Through value ratings and concise reviews, you'll quickly be able to identify the titles that you most want to add to your library.

Because the CD-ROM market is growing so rapidly, we've been adding reviews up until the last moment before this guide went to press. You'll probably see some previews here of titles that aren't even out yet; but don't worry, because if we don't have enough outside feedback, you'll be able to tell. Finally, Andiron Press also has a home page, with some of the latest CD-ROM information, on the World Wide Web.

Let us Hear From You

We hope you enjoy this Guide and find it helpful as you search for CD-ROM titles. And when you do try a new disc, please let us know what you think about it so that we can add your valuable opinion to our database. If you want to fill out our survey and share your opinions of CD-ROMs with others, please send a self-addressed stamped envelope to:

Andiron Press Survey
PO Box 1600
Brookline, MA 02146

Those who complete our written survey by the next book deadline will receive a free copy of the next edition of the book.

If you want to participate in the survey by E-Mail, send an internet message to:

survey@Andiron.com
or examine our web-site at:
http://www.andiron.com.

Chris Shipley, October 1995

TOP RATED PRODUCTS
(OVERALL RATING OVER 20)

24 Echo Lake
24 Wine Guide (Microsoft)
24 Wing Commander III: Heart of the Tiger
23 Bookshelf '95
23 Dark Forces
23 Dr. Seuss's ABC*
23 Jump Start First Grade*
23 Monty Python's Complete Waste of Time
23 Musical Instruments
23 NHL 96*
23 Passage to Vietnam
23 Tortoise and the Hare
23 X-COM: Terror from the Deep
22 7th Guest
22 A.D.A.M. The Inside Story
22 Arthur's Teacher Trouble
22 Dangerous Creatures
22 Descent
22 Dinosaurs!
22 Doom II: Hell on Earth
22 Encarta '95
22 Family Tree Maker Deluxe CD-ROM Edition
22 FIFA Soccer '96*
22 Flight Simulator 5.1
22 Flight Unlimited
22 Fly Fishing: Great Rivers of the West
22 Full Throttle
22 Jump Start Kindergarten
22 Just Grandma and Me
22 KidPix Studio
22 Math Blaster 1: In Search of Spot
22 Math Workshop
22 Mavis Beacon Teaches Typing, Version 3.0
22 Myst
22 New Kid On The Block
22 Oregon Trail II
22 Print Shop Deluxe CD Ensemble
22 Quicken Deluxe 4 for Windows
22 Reader Rabbit's Reading Dev. Library, Level 1*
22 Reader Rabbit's Reading Dev. Library, Level 2*
22 Relentless: Twinsen's Adventure
22 Student Writing Center
22 Super Solvers Gizmos & Gadgets!
22 Thinkin' Things, Collection 2
22 Under a Killing Moon
22 Warcraft: Orcs and Humans

22	Way Things Work
22	Where in the World is Carmen Sandiego?
21	1942 Gold: The Pacific Air War
21	500 Nations
21	75 Seasons: The History of the NFL*
21	Alphabet Blocks
21	Amazing Writing Machine
21	Art Gallery
21	Beginning Reading
21	Berlitz Live! Japanese
21	CardShop Plus! Deluxe
21	Cartoon History of the Universe
21	Cinemania '95
21	Complete Baseball '95
21	Discworld
21	Explorapedia: The World of Nature
21	Fine Artist
21	Flying Colors
21	Freak Show
21	Harry and the Haunted House
21	Incredible Machine 2
21	JFK Assassination: A Visual Investigation
21	Julia Child: Home Cooking with Master Chefs*
21	King's Quest Collector's Edition
21	Links 386 CD
21	Lost Mind of Dr. Brain
21	Math Blaster Mystery: The Great Brain Robbery
21	MusicNet
21	My First Incredible, Amazing Dictionary
21	NASCAR Racing
21	NBA Live '95
21	Nile: Passage to Egypt
21	Passion for Art
21	Peter Pan
21	Reader Rabbit 2
21	RedShift
21	Sammy's Science House
21	San Diego Zoo Presents ... The Animals! 2.0
21	SimCity 2000
21	Spelling Jungle
21	Stephen Biesty's Incredible Cross-Sections Stowaway
21	Storybook Weaver Deluxe
21	Student Writing & Research Center*
21	System Shock
21	Taxi
21	U.S. Navy Fighters
21	Ultimate Football '95
21	Vietnam
21	Virtual Guitar: Welcome to West Feedback*
21	Virtual Pool
21	Where in the USA is Carmen Sandiego?
21	WiggleWorks
21	Your Personal Trainer for the SAT, Version 2.0

*Andiron Rating

KEY TO RATINGS AND SYMBOLS

This sample review explains the information contained
in the Anders CD-ROM Survey:

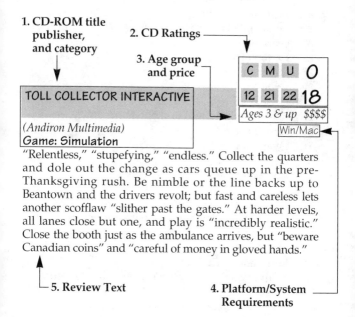

**1. CD-ROM title
publisher,
and category**

2. CD Ratings

**3. Age group
and price**

C	M	U	*O*
12	21	22	**18**

Ages 3 & up $$$$

Win/Mac

TOLL COLLECTOR INTERACTIVE

(Andiron Multimedia)
Game: Simulation

"Relentless," "stupefying," "endless." Collect the quarters
and dole out the change as cars queue up in the pre-
Thanksgiving rush. Be nimble or the line backs up to
Beantown and the drivers revolt; but fast and careless lets
another scofflaw "slither past the gates." At harder levels,
all lanes close but one, and play is "incredibly realistic."
Close the booth just as the ambulance arrives, but "beware
Canadian coins" and "careful of money in gloved hands."

5. Review Text

**4. Platform/System
Requirements**

1. CD-ROM title , publisher and category

2. CD Ratings
We rate discs in four categories:

C Content: How engaging the content of the disc is,
including, when applicable, its plot and the quality and
completeness of the information it contains.

M Multimedia: The quality and appropriate use of sound
and visuals including narration, music, graphics, photos,
videos and animations.

U Usability How easy and pleasant it is to use the CD, how
easily one can navigate its contents, and, when applicable, how successfully interactive it is.

O Overall: Considering everything, the quality of the title.

Content (C), Multimedia (M), Usability (U) and Overall (O) are rated on a scale from 1 to 25 as follows:

> 1 - 5 not worth the spin
> 6 - 10 poor to fair
> 11 - 15 fair to good
> 16 - 20 good to excellent
> 21 - 25 excellent to perfect

Note: Products whose reviews have only a single, Overall rating, had insufficient outside feedback for full ratings. The overall rating in these cases will be printed in lighter type, indicating the review is the opinion of the Andiron Editors. Products whose reviews contain no rating numbers have insufficient outside feedback and have not been examined in sufficient depth by the Andiron Editors to receive a rating. Often such products are just-released, or soon to-be-released.

3. Age Group and Price Range

Age ranges are those recommended by the publisher. These ranges are generally only given for children's titles, although in some cases, titles with mature content will also have an age range noted.

Prices are based on Andiron estimates of street price as follows:

> $ under $30
> $$ $30 to under $45
> $$$ $45 to under $60
> $$$$ $60 to $100
> $$$$$ over $100

> WARNING: It really pays to shop around as prices vary tremendously and change constantly. These ranges are very rough guidelines.

4. Platform and system requirements:

Win = requires a PC running Microsoft Windows 3.1

Mac = requires a Macintosh. Though not always necessary, we assume at least System 7.0.

DOS = requires a PC running DOS version 5.0 or higher

Additional requirements, like CD-drive speed, memory, and sound card, usually exist as well. These guidelines are designed to help you find appropriate titles for your computer, but once you decide on a particular product, be sure to check its system requirements before purchasing it.

5. Review text, based on users feedback and outside reviews.

11 MILLION BUSINESSES PHONE DIRECTORY

19 – 16 **15**

$

American Business Information, Inc.　　　Win/DOS

Phone Directories

This "cheap" CD-ROM "gives lots of data" and in published reviews often finds more businesses than other directories. You can search by business name or phone number, and limit further by city, state or zip. It also lists many fax numbers. But "it could be more robust"—it won't download, omits business classifications and street numbers, and shuts down after you retrieve 5000 numbers. An incomplete business tool, it's probably best as "a useful replacement" for 411.

11TH HOUR: THE SEQUEL TO THE 7TH GUEST

– – –

$$$$

Virgin Interactive Entertainment　　　Win/Mac/DOS

Games/Puzzle & Logic

The name says it all; anticipation is so high for this frequently delayed follow-up to the wildly popular *7th Guest* that the producers make sure we see it right in the title. It's 70 years later, and a string of murders returns players to the Henry Stauf mansion. But this time it takes four CDs to contain all the puzzles, games and quests they need to encounter to solve the crumbling building's mystery. Not for the kids.

1942 GOLD: THE PACIFIC AIR WAR

20 22 16 **21**

$$$

MicroProse Software, Inc.　　　DOS

Games/Combat

This highly regarded war simulation game packs a walloping dose of data, reference and scenarios into its multimedia format. The game is great, There are extras here too, like WWII footage, photos and facts on period planes and pilots and flight tutorials, but "not everyone will be interested" in them. To complicate maneuvers further, it's a DOS game, and the add-ons are all in Windows, so accessing both simultaneously "takes a contortionist."

1995 GROLIER MULTIMEDIA ENCYCLOPEDIA

21 21 19 **20**

$$$

Grolier Electronic Publishing, Inc.　　　Win/Mac/DOS

Reference/Encyclopedias

Based on the Academic American Encyclopedia, with nearly 33,000 articles, more than 5000 of which are new or updated since '94, *Groliers* has "a nice search engine" for easy navigation and is enhanced by very good multimedia. Also, printing is well-integrated with word processors for easy report writing. The "well-written" articles are "best suited to middle and secondary school students." Users "wish you could print/export more of the graphics" and the lack of a dictionary is a "decided disadvantage."

1995 GUINNESS MULTIMEDIA DISC OF RECORDS

19 16 18 **18**

$$

Grolier Electronic Publishing, Inc.　　　Win/Mac

Reference/Encyclopedias

From the Fantastic Feats of Human Creatures to Fantastic Facts of the Animal Kingdom, the Guinness Book records 'em all. The "excellent interface" on this disc searches "from many angles" and facts are "enhanced by interesting, although sparse, multimedia." Long a hit with rabid record readers, the "always fun" Guinness Book is improved upon with "nice graphics." More multimedia, instead of just-the-facts text with most entries, would make a good disc better.

3 FT., 6 PAK FOR KIDS

– ~ –

$

Sirius Publishing, Inc.　　　Win/DOS

Multi-Packs & Collections

This collection of six kid's programs is a low-cost way to get good-quality educational and entertainment titles for your child's library. The package includes *Our House, Cinderella, Dream Team—Spelling Tricks, Lenny's MusicToons,* and *Sing-Along Kids I.*

3-D BODY ADVENTURE

18 21 19 **19**

Ages: 7 & up $$

Knowledge Adventure　　　Win/DOS

Kids/Science

Explore human anatomy and learn about body parts and systems. Select a body organ—the heart for example—and look at it from all angles with the impressive 3-D graphics. While instructions on how to use the CD could be clearer, and the interactive games seem "weak," overall, it's a "great learning tool," a "worthwhile reference for school papers" and "technology at its finest." Thumbs up.

3-D DINOSAUR ADVENTURE

16 16 13 **15**

Ages: 3 & up $$

Knowledge Adventure　　　Win/Mac/DOS

Kids/Science

With 3-D (somewhat "blurry") glasses that help send dinosaurs "menacingly toward you," this title is high on initial multimedia excitement. Some find that after the thrill is gone, these beasts have "bugs" and "only hold kids' attention" for a brief period. Perhaps that's because it seems somewhat "hard to get around" the program. Still, many feel that the visual excitement and realism of the dino movies make this title worth owning.

3D ATLAS

Ages: 7 & up $$$$

Creative Wonders
Geography/Maps

Win/Mac

This is no mere collection of maps. Three globes—political, physical and environmental—can be spun and magnified, and are enhanced with satellite photos, world statistics and time-lapse photography. Some find the easy-to-use interface "limited" and feel the information depth doesn't match print atlases. Users enjoy the "awesome fly-bys" and a "terrific and totally addictive" geography game. A fun enhancement to grade school geography, one teacher's students "begged" to use it.

3D DECK

$$$

Books That Work
House and Garden

Win

This deck-design CD is "do-it-yourself in style," putting the "life" in a Time-Life-type book. Learn to design and build a deck for your home and "see how designs will look and how changes will affect the budget." It starts with several basic deck styles, lets you modify them to suit your tastes, then specifies the materials you'll need. "Helpful videos and animations" talk you through construction tricks. A must-have for anyone considering adding a deck.

3D HOME ARCHITECT

$$$$

Broderbund Software, Inc.
House and Garden

Win

Here's a design tool that's a "snap" to use and "won't let you make mistakes." Even those with "zero drawing ability" can produce accurate blueprints for simple remodeling projects. A spreadsheet estimates job cost and keeps a running tally of necessary materials. Short videos offer design advice. 3D views help you visualize finished projects before you begin. "Amateur architects" enjoy getting "an overview of the field" and use this for "home projects, not for your mansion."

3D LANDSCAPE

$$

Books That Work
House and Garden

Win

Following in the path of do-it-yourself books, this CD helps conceptualize, design and implement landscaping projects. There's an advice section, a resource guide with phone numbers, various estimators (how much concrete do I need?), and a "complicated" Landscape Designer for seeing your work. The title's "much harder to use than expected" and has got some installation bugs. Nevertheless, it's an "aid in long range projects." A good crop of features requiring lots of harvesting time.

4 PAWS OF CRAB: AN INTERACTIVE THAI COOKBOOK

$

Live Oak Multimedia Win/Mac
Cooking & Food

"Entertaining," "cool," "sophisticated." Users love it, though some admit they "don't know what the point is." A Thai cookbook and a "journey" as well, this artful disc mingles recollections of a Thai cook and an American exchange student with day-to-day life, history and food, using stories, photos, street sounds and narration (but "choppy" video). The cookbook has "good" meals, but with only 40 recipes, it's not comprehensive, and some lament the "lack" of basic dishes.

5 FT. 10 PAK SPECIAL EDITION
5 FT. 10 PAK COLLECTOR'S EDITION

– – –
$$

Sirius Publishing, Inc Win/DOS
Multi-Packs & Collections

Dust off those old CDs, repackage them in a five-foot-long fold-out case, and you've got two hot new collections well worth the low price. Disks in the Special Edition include *Beyond Planet Earth, Who Shot Johnny Rock? 1994 Sports Illustrated Almanac, Hell Cab, PrintMaster Gold, Microsoft Multimedia Mozart,* and *National Parks of America.* Some titles in the Collector's Edition are: *Introduction to Classical Music, Prince Interactive, Journeyman Project Turbo,* and *Mad Dog McCree* and also (under slightly different names) *Webster's Interactive Encyclopedia* and *Dr. Ruth's Encyclopedia of Sex.* An exceptional value for anyone hunting one or two of these titles, as they'll get the others virtually for free.

5 FT., 10 PAK, VOLUME 1

– – –
$$

Sirius Publishing, Inc Win
Multi-Packs & Collections

This perennial bestseller lines 10 CDs end-to-end to deliver five feet of trusty, if somewhat rusty titles. Containing once-popular but now remaindered titles including *Kings Quest V, Time Man of the Year, World Vista Atlas,* and *Doom.* Not as good a set as more recent collections, like the Special Edition and Collectors Edition, also reviewed here.

5 FT., 10 PAK, VOLUME 2

– – –
$$

Sirius Publishing, Inc Win/DOS
Multi-Packs & Collections

Like any sequel, the concept's the same but the content doesn't quite match The Original. The *5 Ft., 10 Pak, Volume Two* reached into the seconds bin a second time and came up with "a few winners:" *Battle Chess, Dr. Schueler's Home Medical Advisor* (taken from version 3 non-multimedia diskettes), and *Space Quest IV.* But most of the discs are just fair. As with the Original, buy it if it contains a disc you'd otherwise purchase separately.

500 NATIONS

20 22 20 **21**
$$
Microsoft Corporation — Win/Mac

History

Actor Kevin Costner is your host in this compelling, "sensitive look" at Native American Indian culture, based on a CBS documentary. Using archival photos, 3-D animation that reconstructs Native-American cities, and video interviews, it's visually "remarkable." "Annoyingly," the navigation has numerous dead-ends, and the text is spare, but it still effectively showcases the "incredibly deep" content. History buffs might like a bibliography, but quibbles aside, here's a "powerful" and "shocking" success.

70 MILLION HOUSEHOLDS PHONE BOOK

13 – 9 **11**
$
American Business Information, Inc. — Win/DOS

Phone Directories

This limited, inexpensive two-disc set leaves many feeling it's worth spending "the extra $20" for a better phone disc. Like other major phone CDs, it excludes unlisted numbers; unlike them, it also excludes people who've removed themselves from mailing lists. The "less than desirable" searching permits reverse searches, or searches by name, but name searches require adding city, state or zip. Addresses exclude street numbers, listings can't be downloaded and, after retrieving 5000 numbers, the program self-destructs.

75 SEASONS: THE HISTORY OF THE NFL

– – – **21**
$$
RealTime Sports — Mac/DOS

Sports Reference

A sweeping saga of TV miniseries proportions, *75 Seasons* is a colorful, nostalgic and introspective view of the National Football League. Using a unique interactive movie player, the user can watch more than 90 minutes of video from start to finish, or leapfrog from one era to another, viewing films, reading articles or checking stats. Pat Summerall is perfectly cast as commentator, and the interviews with legends like Sammy Baugh and Sid Luckman are priceless.

7TH GUEST

22 23 22 **22**
$$$
Virgin Interactive Entertainment — Mac/DOS

Games/Puzzle & Logic

This "exciting" two-disc "mystery buff's" delight is a megahit. It begins as six guests (and you) mysteriously convene in a haunted house. Why? Begin your quest for the answer by exploring rooms and solving "challenging" puzzles. "A bit gruesome" for kids and "a bit slow" for the less patient. Reaction to brain-teasers varies from "extremely" hard to "just right." The "spectacular graphics," "spooky" music and videos run best on faster machines. A "great game."

800 NUMBER PHONE BOOK

— — — 14
$

American Business Information, Inc.   Win/DOS
Phone Directories

The second entry in the 800-number field, this single disc has 250,000 listings, taken directly from the tapes of the AT&T 800-number directory. Many 800 numbers, including many tech support numbers, are unlisted or are not from AT&T, so don't expect to find everything here. Searches, by name or toll-free phone number only, and listings, without streets or business classification, are both more limited than *FreePhone*, and after retrieving 5000 listings, the program commits hara-kiri.

A.D.A.M. THE INSIDE STORY

22 21 22 **22**
$$

A.D.A.M. Software, Inc.   Win/Mac
Science/Anatomy

Bone up on body basics: head for The Animated Dissection of Anatomy for Medicine. Click to see how the leg bone's connected to the hip bone. Although some feel control icons could be friendlier, it's "detailed, informative and entertaining," with "elegant" drawings and "excellent" sound and a Family Scrapbook that examines physiological functions. It's not a medical text, but it's great for those who really want to get under their skin and see what's there.

AAA TRIP PLANNER

14 8 13 **14**
$$

Compton's NewMedia   Win/DOS
Travel/Maps & Atlases

Road trippers have long depended on Triple-A for directions. In this CD they'll find plenty of clear, accurate road trip guidance that "comes in handy," including "detailed information on restaurants and hotels." But be warned before turning in this CD's direction: "it can't display the entire route on the screen," it lacks multimedia content, "a disappointment considering the price," and, unlike other trip-planning CDs, it won't combine text directions, maps, and attractions in one printout.

ACES OF THE DEEP

20 20 17 **20**
$$$

Sierra On-Line, Inc.   DOS
Games/Combat

The Battle of the North Atlantic was a daunting experience for German U-boat commanders. Installing and piloting this intricate, ambitious simulation will be the same for gamers, especially getting the hang of all the controls ("You really need the manual with this one.") "Great graphics" and accurate sound effects combine for "an intense experience"—"I'm completely addicted"—but only after fighting "tooth and nail" to get it to run properly.

ACES: THE COMPLETE COLLECTOR'S EDITION

– – – 18
$$$
DOS

Sierra On-Line, Inc.
Games/Combat
Each of these simulated aviation battle games are "variations on a theme." The planes and scenery change from the early barnstormers in *Aviation Pioneers*, featuring vintage photographs and video clips, to modern heavy bombers in *A-10 Tank Killer*. Also included are *Aces over Europe*, *Aces of the Pacific*, and *The Red Baron*. They "don't take much time to learn," and, with "good" graphics, the "many varied missions" are "interesting and entertaining," putting you up against "some great aces."

ADVENTURES OF HYPERMAN

16 20 19 **17**
Ages: 7-14 $$
Win

IBM Multimedia Studio
Kids/Edugames-Science
Kids may be bowled over by the "really cool" animation and sounds of this interactive learning adventure that looks "like a Saturday morning cartoon" only "more educational." Click on the terrarium's water icon to shift climates from arid to tropical; click on the microscope to enlarge a hairball 1000 times. Yet five science puzzles' "lack of action" and "simplicity" might underwhelm. The "klutzy" Hyperman character is funny, but probably won't hold a child's interest for long.

ADVENTURES WITH OSLO: TOOLS AND GADGETS

18 15 18 **18**
Ages: 5-14 $
Win/Mac

Science for Kids
Kids/Science
Oslo the Robotron guides children through a "fun," "ambitious" and "informative" multimedia introduction to light machinery. Youngsters enjoy the coloring and the animated storybook, in which they can rescue Dolly the Llama by choosing the right tools. Older kids explore Maze Arcade, where problem-solving and mechanics come into play, as more complex mazes and machines are used to demonstrate the workings of wedges, wheels, screws, pulleys and more.

AIR HAVOC CONTROLLER

17 20 19 **20**
$$
Win

Trimark Interactive
Games/Simulation
You aced the controls of that flight simulator, but what about landing 60 different aircraft in 30 minutes? Familiar with the word "panic?" As an air traffic controller, success depends on skill, "lots of practice," and "tremendous attention to detail." Don't let impressive 3-D graphics distract you. You get credit for safe landings; but near misses and mid-air collisions are, as they say, on your head. "No weekend flying here."

ALADDIN ACTIVITY CENTER

20 21 21 **20**

Ages: 5 & up $

Disney Interactive   Win/Mac
Kids/Edugames-General

Based on the animated Disney film, this activity pack is a real hit with fans of the movie. The quantity and quality of its activities are good enough to keep kids quite busy, and the six video clips are entertaining. While some experience a few glitches, such as "screen freezes," and claim that the Genie "could use a vocabulary lesson," most admit the "kids love it," and it's reasonably educational. Best for 5-10 year olds.

ALGE-BLASTER 3

19 17 16 **17**

Ages: 12 & up $$

Davidson & Associates, Inc.   Win/Mac
Kids/Edugames-Math

Players solve algebraic equations, learn graphing and translate word problems into usable formulas—all to defend Planet Quadratica from aliens. In Red Alert, for example, invaders drop from the sky; by changing the angle (or slope) of a cannon, kids try to blow them up. All told, there are 4 games, an "in-depth," though not-always-easy tutorial and a "hefty" glossary. Using "neat" arcade-style graphics, this program "livens up" algebra, making it a "favorite math tutor."

ALIEN TALES

20 19 18 **20**

Ages: 9-14 $$

Broderbund Software, Inc.   Win/Mac
Kids/Edugames-Reading

Conquer aliens (and spark a passion for literature) by answering questions on some 30 classical and contemporary works of young adult fiction (450 excerpts contained on the disc). Featuring such authors as Mark Twain, E.B. White, Roald Dahl and Judy Blume, as well as "obnoxious" alien impostors, these quiz show-style games "are awesome!" The disc wins raves with its colorful graphics and "fun sounds." It makes "answering comprehension questions enjoyable."

ALIENS

- - -

$$$

Mindscape   DOS
Games/Combat

It's about time someone launched a CD on the space horror films starring Sigourney Weaver and the deadly, slobbering creature that pursued her. Based on the Dark Horse comics that were inspired by the movies, the aliens are destroying an entire population of settlers and players need to discover an even deadlier force that is terrifying the aliens themselves.

ALISTAIR AND THE ALIEN INVASION   18 19 17 **18**

Ages 5-10 $

Simon & Schuster Interactive   Win/Mac
Kids/Stories

Alistair travels the universe pursuing an interesting plant for school and winds up saving earth from aliens. Based on Marilyn Sanders' wonderful book, the disc will read to you, with or without clickable animations, or you can go on an Alien Plant Quest. But it's not much of a quest—it just means clicking on plants in Alistair's room. Also, goofy sounds and "gorgeous" graphics don't make up for "shallow" activities and "limited interaction." Buy the book instead.

ALL-IN-ONE LANGUAGE FUN!   19 18 19 **19**

Ages: 3-12 $

Syracuse Language Systems   Win/Mac
Language

Parlez-vous ROM-eze? Even before the computer age (when was that?) linguists knew that the best way to learn new languages was the audio-visual method. No translating—just listening, watching, responding… and *voila*, instant dialogue! These techniques are used here to introduce Spanish, French, German, Japanese and English. Gentle prompts from tutors encourage participation in the format of simple games like Bingo and Simon Says. Intense, *oui*—but also fun. Reading skills aren't necessary.

ALL-STAR BASEBALL   – – – **16**

$$

Accolade, Inc.   Win/Mac
Games/Sports Simulation

All-Star Baseball just says "Play Ball!" with American and National League all-stars, TV-style interface, live action video, CD-quality sound effects and play-by-play with Al Michaels and Tim McCarver. The video play speed is quite fast; however, lengthy delays while the program finds the proper sequence are very annoying. The TV-style interface works smoothly and the presentation is visually impressive, but a lack of depth limits this game to occasional play.

ALLIE'S ACTIVITY KIT   18 17 19 **17**

Ages: 3-8 $$

Opcode Interactive   Win
Kids/Early Learning Skills

Like its predecessor, *Allie's Playhouse*, this kit is made up of 16 wide-ranging problem-solving activities that kids find enjoyable. Unlike *Playhouse*, however, there is less emphasis on music and more on visual activities, including a highly favored creative geography game. Not the fanciest production, but a "very good overall value" with a nice, large array of engaging, educational activities, best for very young kids.

23

ALLIE'S PLAYHOUSE

21 20 21 **20**

Ages: 3-8 $$

Opcode Interactive Win/Mac

Kids/Early Learning Skills

Sixteen early learning activities, found by clicking inside a playhouse, make this a "cute presentation" for the very young computer novice. Even tots find it "easy to use" and "fun," with lots of program choices. Parents would like more depth, such as "more pages to color" in the coloring book and added levels of difficulty, and report some program bugs. "There is no goal," so a bit of adult support will certainly help motivate young users.

ALONE IN THE DARK 3

14 14 12 **14**

Ages: 12 & up $$$

I-MOTION, Inc. DOS

Games/Role-playing & Interactive Fiction

On location in Slaughter Gulch, the movie crew's kidnapped by ghosts—and you, Edward Carnby, private eye of the supernatural—must dig up clues, solve puzzles and shoot zombies to save them. Some prefer it to *AITD 1* and *2* for "smooth" motion, a "more elaborate" story, and the "right blend of chills and humor." Others say "3 is awful!" The controls are only slightly easier, and the weird "camera angles" make aim and shoot a nightmare.

ALPHABET BLOCKS

21 22 22 **21**

Ages: 3-6 $

Sierra On-Line, Inc. Win/Mac

Kids/Early Learning Skills

Using the alphabet, upper and lower case, cartoon characters take kids to two game areas, where they learn sight and sound letter recognition. Kids go "crazy over" the characters that scoot across the screen when they get the right answer. Parents like the way the characters mouth the sounds so that "you can practically read their lips." This "excellent" age-appropriate tool helps pre-readers absorb the important "sound and symbol relationships."

ALPHABONK FARM

17 17 15 **17**

Ages: 3 & up $$

Headbone Interactive Inc. Win/Mac

Kids/Early Learning Skills

This title teaches spelling and word association through images, sound and games. At the speed it works, however, it might also be a lesson in patience. One parent complains her child became "the 'mad clicker' trying to get this program to react." Others wonder "just how much the kids are really learning." Learning aside, it has good graphics, some age-appropriate ribald humor, and is "a funny and irreverent romp through a wacky farmyard" better appreciated by adults than by kids.

AMAZING ANIMATION

19 21 19 **19**

Ages: 5-12 $$

Claris Corp. Mac

Kids/Art & Writing

Kids will love creating their own animated movies using template backgrounds, objects and sounds. They can also design their own elements with the full-color paint tool. The bold and friendly interface has a 'Little Kids' mode, allowing even the youngest family member to join the fun. Although it could use "more ready-made backgrounds," and the clip art selection is more limited than like-minded programs, it's a "wonderful way" for kids to be creative.

AMAZING WRITING MACHINE

23 21 20 **21**

Ages: 6-12 $$

Broderbund Software, Inc. Win/Mac

Kids/Art & Writing

This "truly amazing" program eliminates every writer's nemesis: "the blank page." With templates for stories, letters, journals, essays and poems, young wordsmiths start from scratch or 'spin' to get "prebuilt" compositions that give choices of key words. Use *KidPix* tools for illustrating, an "ideas" button for creative inspiration, and passwords to protect journals. The Infosaurus rhymes are entertaining, but does moon really rhyme with shampoo? Well, why quibble? This is a "powerful, fun tool."

AMAZON TRAIL

21 21 19 **20**

Ages: 10-16 $$

MECC Win/Mac/DOS

Kids/Edugames-Social Studies

Kids go on an epic quest to save the Inc.as, while learning about the terrain, people and wildlife of the South America rain forests. Gather treasures by exploring and trading en route while searching for an anti-malaria drug to help the plague-ridden secret Inc.an city. This "exciting CD makes learning fun and interesting," though teens might find the pace too slow. Also, it's not for the faint of heart: even children characters can get sick and die.

AMERICA'S CIVIL WAR: A NATION DIVIDED

14 9 9 **11**

$

Softkey International Win

History/War

There's tons of information on this title, but the "atrocious interface makes this CD almost unusable." After mastering the intricate search commands, you'll find the action slow and the windows squinty and, with only eight short videos, there's little multimedia. But the "biggest disappointment" is the text, which is frequently skimpy and fails to put events in context. This is "truly horrific shovelware" that even "dedicated civil war buffs should avoid like the plague."

AMERICAN HERITAGE TALKING DICTIONARY

22 21 21 20
$$
Softkey International — Win/Mac
Reference/Dictionaries
"Bye-bye to those funny pronunciation marks!" With definitions of 200,000 word, 72,000 are e*nun*ci*at*ed in dul*ci*mate tones by human voices. This "excellent resource" lets you search for words even when uncertain of the spelling. It includes a thesaurus as well as rhyme and anagram finders. You can search by topic and meaning when you have that frustrating can't-find-the-right-word feeling. By the way, you get virtually the same dictionary with *Microsoft Bookshelf*.

AMERICAN SIGN LANGUAGE DICTIONARY ON CD-ROM

21 18 19 18
$$$
HarperCollins Interactive — Win/Mac
Language
This reference work is "hands down, the easiest way to learn" signing. Containing over 2000 signs, there's "lots of information," here, and it's "well broken down." With robust searching, practice games and actual videos of gestures, this disc "expands your command of ASL" more interactively than any book. But before paying the hefty price, it's worth remembering that, as when learning any language, "you have to have an interest in the area" to stay involved.

AMERICAN VISIONS

21 20 14 18
$$$
Creative Labs — Win/Mac
Art Appreciation
This attempt to show "modern art in a very modern way," results in a "quirky interface," that's "confusing and frustrating" to use. But once you find it, the content is "impressive and engrossing." With "excellent" reproductions of works by such greats as Arthur Dove, Charles Demuth and Roy Lichtenstein, it includes "hard to find videos" containing commentary from artists, critics and art historians. All told, it's a disjointed presentation of "stunningly beautiful" material.

AMERICAN WHITE PAGES, 1995 EDITION

- - - 17
$$$
American Business Information, Inc. — Win
Phone Directories
This five-disc set is a more powerful cousin to the *70 Million Households* CD. The listings are similar, but here include full street address, and two unique new factoids: length of residence, and the enticing median home value, actually just the median for all homes in the area. The program has several search functions, including by name alone, but can't search by phone number. And though entries are downloadable, after 5000 numbers, the program expires.

AMERICAN YELLOW PAGES, 1995 EDITION

– – – **17**
$$$
Win

American Business Information, Inc.

Phone Directories

The big brother of the *11 Million Businesses* CD, this single disc is enhanced by listings that include full street addresses and categorization through 7500 searchable business classifications, by far the most of any phone CD. Uniquely, it also has some fax numbers, and even gives the approximate size of Yellow Pages ads. But unlike other offerings, there is no reverse number searching, and after furnishing 5000 listings, the program bites the dust.

ANCIENT LANDS

20 18 20 **20**
$$

Microsoft Corporation
Win/Mac

History

Ancient Greece, Egypt and Rome come alive in this well-designed title. From Pharaoh to slave, you'll learn about the people, ideas and events of these vanished empires. National Geographic video footage combines with quirky, "beautiful" graphics, absorbing audio, and such "grainy" movie clips as Elizabeth Taylor's classic *Cleopatra*. This "all information and history" title is meant for the history buff, so if you're likely to complain about "no activities," stay away from *Ancient Lands*.

ANIMALS!, VERSION 2.0

21 22 21 **21**

See *San Diego Zoo Presents … The Animals! Version 2.0.*

ANNATOMMY: AN ADVENTURE INTO THE HUMAN BODY

12 13 12 **11**
Ages: 8 & up $
Win

IVI, Inc.

Kids/Edugames-Science

Two children, science know-it-all's Anna and Tommy, take a spaceship journey through the human body. Their voyage, based on "realistic footage," gives a comprehensive look at the body, from the aorta to the spleen. But it's "crudely animated and exasperating to navigate" and the games don't "require you to use any knowledge that you gained from the program." This is a "failed experiment at grafting together video games and anatomy lessons."

ANNO'S LEARNING GAMES

18 19 16 **17**
Ages: 6-10 $
Win/Mac

Putnam New Media

Kids/Edugames-General

Kriss and Kross are helpful elves that guide kids through seven math and logic based games, including a numerical ordering game, a geometric puzzle game, and a nonsense poem-making activity. With "beautiful illustrations," high-quality animations and "the best" sound, these "really fun" games are varied enough for most kids to find something to do here. "Younger children might need some help," and some reading is necessary.

ANTARCTICA

Cambrix Publishing
Science/Animals

Tackling a topic that few users are familiar with, *Antarctica* uses video clips, photos and audio to paint a picture of this vast frozen continent. Users are shown the effects of global warming, the animals who survive in this climate, and the people who have braved it. Though the presentation sometimes seems "a bit rushed," and would benefit from "more extensive multimedia," the photos are "clean and sharp" and the interface is straightforward.

ARCADE MANIA

Corel Corporation
Games/Arcade

Save your quarters for these three space-age arcade games: Neutrino, a modern-day pong with a twist; Lunar Fox, a 3-D tank combat game; and Nova 3, an alien shoot-'em-up. Each game is preceded by awesome sounds and a touch of splotchy video to set the stage. Game play is fast and fun, and requires no extra game hardware. A nice addition to any arcade fan's game collection.

ARCHIBALD'S GUIDE TO THE MYSTERIES OF ANCIENT EGYPT

Swfte International, Ltd.
History

While it's "no technical marvel," this CD is a "very accurate" children's guide to Ancient Egypt and the mysteries of hieroglyphics. Little Archibald takes budding Egyptologists through this ancient world, showing them film clips and photos, and teaching them hieroglyphics. Most find the interface "easy to use," though the numerous features might confuse younger children. The graphics are unimpressive but, whether or not the subject is practical, there's lots of "good content."

ARE YOU AFRAID OF THE DARK? THE TALE OF ORPHEO'S CURSE

Viacom Interactive Media
Games/Role-playing & Interactive Fiction

Fans of Nickelodeon TV's *Are You Afraid Of The Dark* instantly recognize the main characters—members of The Midnight Society—who show up in digitized video to guide a girl and her brother safely to one of the program's multiple endings. There's no gore, and parents say that their kids "love the program"—but "frustration can set in very quickly" when they "are unable to locate the enchanted objects" or, horror of horrors … when the software crashes.

ARMORED FIST

Nova Logic, Inc.
Games/Combat
Deafening blasts, the heat, the oily smells of maneuvers…
this is as close as tank sims get to realism. More interesting
than its predecessor, *Comanche: Maximum Overkill*, this title
appeals to armchair generals (command up to 16 vehicles
at once), despite having "too many things to do." Non-
strategists enjoy gunning engines and demolishing enemy
targets, "though only an octopus could follow the manual." The graphics are a "disappointment," becoming
wildly distorted the closer objects get.

AROUND THE WORLD IN 80 DAYS

Creative Wonders
Kids/Edugames-Social Studies
A major component of multimedia is interaction—something this title sorely lacks. The graphics are mediocre, the
sound is unimpressive, and the entire package is boring
and condescending to kids. "I guess I expect too much
from these programs, but when I'm paying 40 or 50 bucks
for something, I want a little more interaction than to
be dragged all over the world by the one or two choices
they offer."

ART GALLERY

Microsoft Corporation
Art Appreciation
This "treasure trove of more than 2000 paintings" from
London's National Gallery brings "art to life" with animations showing such things as how paintings are restored.
Though it "looks like an encyclopedia," a "dry walk in the
park" rather than a stroll through a museum, reproduc-
tions are surprisingly crisp on the small screen. There's lots
and lots of art to see as well as historical background and
biographies.

ART OF MAKING GREAT PASTRIES

Arome Interactive
Cooking & Food
Based on 101 pastry recipes from Thuries, a French magazine, reviewers find this a more "step-by-step approach"
than its companion, *Four Seasons of French Gourmet Cuisine*.
The disc competently leads would-be chefs through the
necessary basics of creams, cakes and dough, and sinful
photos practically compel visits to "the nearest bakery."
Still, "tiny" video lessons make "difficult" viewing, and
recipes are awkwardly displayed on-screen.

ARTHUR'S BIRTHDAY
19 22 21 20

Ages: 6-10 $$

Living Books   Win/Mac
Kids/Stories

Arthur's Birthday party is the same day as his friend's and, as the story progresses, he makes everyone happy by working out a solution to this dilemma. Part of the Living Books series in which scenes are filled with click-activated animations and words are highlighted as they're read aloud to aid begining readers, this "cute" story is narrated in Spanish and English. "Well-executed," with "amusing," sometimes musical, animations, this title keep kids "entertained…for hours."

ARTHUR'S TEACHER TROUBLE
21 22 22 22

Ages: 6-10 $$

Living Books   Win/Mac
Kids/Stories

Kids follow along as Arthur faces the "trials and tribulations" of school and home life. No child escapes home and school trouble-free, which makes this "wonderful" and "hilarious" title especially endearing. As with all the Living Books, it's filled with animated clickable objects and words are highlighted as they're read aloud to aid beginning readers. This one is narrated in Spanish and English and to some "the best of all the Living Books."

ASTRONOMICA: THE QUEST FOR THE EDGE OF THE UNIVERSE
16 18 13 15

Ages: 9-17 $$

Hyper-Quest, Inc.   Win/Mac
Science/Astronomy

Learning astronomy is the goal here, via 27 games tied to finding a missing scientist in an observatory. With "pretty graphics" and "neat eerie music," it tries to "integrate a *Myst*-like game" with learning. Navigating is slow, and you may walk around a lot. You'll often need to look up facts in the reference area, inspiring some to say it's more "a flash-card drill than a game." Still, for high-school space buffs, "challenging puzzles" might be "an excellent reason to explore our universe."

ATARI 2600 ACTION PACK
- - - 12

$

Activision   Win/Mac
Games/Arcade

Like dusting off the old Victorola and playing Glenn Miller albums, the appeal here is "pure nostalgia." Open the time capsule for *Action Pack 1* and out pops such worn-out Atari oldies as 'Chopper Command' and 'Kaboom!' *Action Pack 2* scores some points with 'Ice Hockey' and 'Megamania,' but why revive 'Plaque Attack' and 'Oink?' Ironically, these simplistic relics "play abysmally slow," despite today's speedy PC technology. "A complete miss."

ATARI 2600 ACTION PACK 2

– – –

Activision
Games/Arcade
See *Atari 2600 Action Pack.*

$
Win/Mac

AUTOMANIA: THE ULTIMATE CAR BUYING GUIDE

– – – **16**

Creative Multimedia Corporation
Consumer Guides

$
Win

Car magazines have gone interactive, and it's a boon to those who dread the dealership. *Automania* supplies specifications for over 1,600 vehicles plus photos, a few videos, and reviews from the experts at Automobile magazine. Users say "it gives good background" on makes and models, with information ranging from engines to airbags to "trade-in values." This simple and "quick" package has "everything" you'll need to know about "your ideal car."

AUTOMAP ROAD ATLAS

20 19 18 **19**

Microsoft Corporation
Travel/Maps & Atlases

$$
Win

No food, water or rest stops required for this co-pilot! Most mapping programs are just ho-hum, but this one is "exceptional." "Astoundingly accurate" with trip times listed to the minute, *Automap's* detailed maps also list a "great deal" of additional information like gas stations and interesting detours along the route. But unless you have a powerful laptop, don't leave home before printing out the user-friendly driving instructions and maps.

AVIATION ADVENTURE

14 15 13 **14**

Knowledge Adventure
Kids/Science

Ages: 8 & up $
Win/DOS

If you love the noise, speed and grandeur of airplanes, you'll be pleased to find this title "packed with" an "extensive" reference library and "interesting" encyclopedia of planes. But, while it provides all the information, the disc tends to lecture—there's "not enough interactivity" for younger users. Tracing the history of planes from World War II bombers to the 2000-mile-per-hour SR-71 Blackbird, it highlights changes in the design and technology of planes over the years.

BAD DAY ON THE MIDWAY

− − −

$$$
iNscape Win/Mac
Avant Garde
The award-winning illustrator and animator, Jim Ludtke, whose *Freak Show* was last year's smash digiterati hit, is back with a follow-up that's being described as "Disneyland of the Damned." This sinister soap opera is set in an other-worldly theme park where players take on the points of view of the various Midway inhabitants in order to piece together the puzzles of a deadly mystery. The soundtrack is supplied by the San Francisco cult band The Residents.

BAILEY'S BOOK HOUSE

19 19 21 **19**

Ages: 2-6 $$
Edmark Corporation Win/Mac/DOS
Kids/Early Learning Skills
These five "easy-to-use" activities, with "clear" speech and graphics, are "a joy." The Letter Machine creates a sentence starting with a chosen letter. Make-a-Story prompts kids to complete sentence blanks with pictures, and then reads the stories back. Kid Cards, a favorite, promotes independence by giving youngsters tools like pre-fab messages and stamps, to create cards they can easily print themselves. "Not glitzy," but it's a "fun," "ideal first language program."

BARBIE AND HER MAGICAL HOUSE

16 21 21 **19**

$$
Hi Tech Entertainment, Inc. Win/Mac
Kids/General
Barbie's world is as pink as ever. Kids explore her home, making objects "magically spring to life." There are occasional games, like the jigsaw puzzle in the kitchen, but the highlight is going to her bedroom and dressing her up. Choose hairstyle, make-up, clothing and jewelry—and presto, she's changed! No more frustrating struggles to yank on her skintight outfits. Barbie is strictly 2-D and could use "better dialogue," but if you've already got a dozen dolls, this is probably "a must."

BARRON'S PROFILES OF AMERICAN COLLEGES

− − − 16

$$
Laser Resources, Inc. Win/Mac
Consumer Guides
The scary process of choosing colleges is made "a little easier" with this CD. Though decidedly short on multimedia pizzazz, with just a few promotional videos, it's a "powerful," "easy to use" tool that lets applicants sift through the 1,650 U.S. schools using any criteria. Copies of applications and curriculum catalogs are included for a small number of schools. Like the book, *Barrons* gives you just the facts; for a college's character you still have to look elsewhere.

BASEBALL FOR WINDOWS — ERNIE HARWELL BROADCAST BLAST

– – – **19**

$$$

Miller Associates Win
Games/Sports Simulation

This title introduces "live" broadcast audio to computer baseball, using RichSound, an amazing technology that searches thousands of sound bites to produce lifelike play-by-play dialogue. Legendary Detroit Tigers' broadcaster Ernie Harwell serves up old-time radio baseball, complete with player names, rare plays, vendor calls and a host of amusing special effects. Ernie's delivery even changes in the late innings, as the fans implore their home town heroes to pull one out in the ninth.

BASEBALL TONIGHT

16 17 13 **15**

$$

See *ESPN Baseball Tonight*.

BASEBALL'S GREATEST HITS

19 17 17 **19**

$$

Voyager Company Win/Mac
Sports Reference

Wish you were there when Babe Ruth called his historic home run? This "labor of love" CD takes you close, with "entertaining" historical footage, still photography, stats and audio clips. Watch and listen to legends like Hank Aaron, Ty Cobb, Jackie Robinson and the immortal Babe in this trip down Baseball's memory lane. For fans, there's great nostalgic value…on a par with rare trading cards.

BATTLE BEAST

– – –

$$$

7th Level Win
Games/Arcade

A Saturday morning cartoon of a game complete with morphing heroes, funky background music, and knockout fight sequences. Fight renegade Battle Beasts, kill deadly toads to advance to increasingly difficult levels and ultimately to a duel with the evil Toadman. You'll want to spend time with the manual and practice in 'boot camp' before going into war. Keyboard control is awkward and it can take hours to master even basic moves.

BATTLECRUISER 3000 A.D.

– – –

$$$$

Take 2 Interactive Software, Inc. DOS
Games/Combat

PC-ers have known about this one for four years now—that's how long it's taken to produce this huge combination strategic conquest space flight-simulation ground-based combat game. As a battlecruiser commander, you are responsible for a 125-member crew, five ship decks, seven computer systems, and a galaxy of 225 planets. Sign on personnel, take prisoners, buy and trade resources, declare war, explore planets. Phew! Better take a nap first.

BATTLEDROME

11 12 10 **12**
$$

Sierra On-Line, Inc. DOS
Games/Combat

Negotiate the terms and the weapons, and then it's one-on-one in the Battledrome arena, using your giant armored robot to pound your opponent's robot into scrap. Prepare: you'll need practice with the "overly complex interface" controls for movement, shields and weapons. Single-player mode is "pretty dull" with "not much replay value," but if you use the game's modem and network-readiness, and challenge a friend, then you'll start cookin'.

BEAST WITHIN

– – –
$$$

Sierra On-Line, Inc. Win/Mac
Games/Role-playing & Interactive Fiction

Who says PC games aren't highbrow enough? An entire opera was written for the soundtrack of this second installment in the Gabriel Knight series. This time, the Shadow Hunter travels from a New Orleans bookstore to a Bavarian town where he's been enlisted by the villagers to find and destroy what they believe to be a werewolf. Okay, so it's not 'La Boheme.' Also, it's not for youngsters.

BEAUTY OF JAPAN THROUGH THE ART OF SUSHI

– – – 12
$$

Arome Interactive Win/Mac
Cooking & Food

Do you have a yen for sushi? Want to study its history, learn how to arrange, cut and prepare it? Here's the only CD that purports to teach you. But attractive photos and austere, elegantly designed screens can't disguise the confusing and often limited contents. Aside from narration of the onscreen text, the multimedia is sparse. Even the elaborately described 27-step Tea Ceremony has just a few marginally helpful videos. Buy a book instead.

BEAVIS AND BUTT-HEAD IN VIRTUAL STUPIDITY

– – –

See *MTV's Beavis and Butt-head in Virtual Stupidity.*

BEER HOMEBREWING GUIDE

16 5 16 **15**
$

Walnut Creek CDROM Win
Wine, Beer & Spirits

Do wort aromas turn you on? Are you secretly terrified of boil-overs and syrup burns? Look no farther, lagerman, here's the title for you. This proudly amateurish CD has some "not so great pictures," step by step instructions, recipes, mail order catalogs and a very bizarre compilation of Internet beer postings. The *Homebrewing Guide* will please "really serious homebrew junkies," but leave less foamy fanatics complaining it's a "real bunch of Barley."

BEER HUNTER

18 19 15 **17**

$$

Discovery Home Entertainment Win/Mac
Wine, Beer & Spirits

British beer-ologist Michael Jackson walks you through the history and art of beer-making, with emphasis on the boutique breweries of the United States. The interface is a simulated field guide allowing you to identify and classify a Beaver Tail Brown Ale from twenty paces. Jot down your own observations in the "intoxicating electronic picture book" notebook. Events, periodicals and other resources are provided. *Beer Hunter* is "a flavorful overview" for those with an adventurous palate.

BEGINNING READING

21 20 22 **21**

Ages: 3-7 $

Sierra On-Line, Inc. Win/Mac
Kids/Edugames-Reading

It may seem innocent but this crafty package makes words into playtime, building reading skills along the way. Three activities focus on alphabetizing, letter sounds with rhyming, and reading with fill-in-the-blank stories. Though it's a simple program with simple graphics, *Beginning Reading* is well-designed to reinforces basic language skills. It's "very easy" for little guys to grasp, and one teacher rated it the "best early reading program" she'd seen.

BERENSTAIN BEARS GET IN A FIGHT

19 18 20 **20**

Ages: 3-10 $$

Living Books Win/Mac
Kids/Stories

The "always amusing" *Berenstain Bears* are teaching a lesson in tolerance and manners. Colorful graphics unfold with each screen as kids hear the story told or play with "cute" clickable animations. The pages turn quickly and the 10 added songs are a plus: funny, peppy, sing-a-long tunes. But somewhat dry narration means that some of the humor of the book is lost in the transition to CD. Not quite up there with the best of the Living Books, it's still "a very good program."

BERLITZ LIVE! JAPANESE

21 22 21 **21**

$$$$$

Sierra On-Line, Inc. Win/Mac
Language/Japanese

Heading east? Have a yearning for Yen? You won't go wrong with this "quick route" to picking up key words and phrases. Visually stunning, with good music and "friendly animated characters," these 12 lessons focus on everyday activities like eating out and using the phone for business. A cartoon *sensei*, or teacher, narrates dialogues and instructions. You follow his lip movements to learn pronunciation. "Helpful tips" make it "a great guide to Japanese culture" as well.

BERLITZ LIVE! SPANISH
20 19 20 **20**

$$$$

Sierra On-Line, Inc.   Win/Mac
Language/Spanish

A title that makes frustrated travelers cry for joy, this admirably captures the "tried-and-true Berlitz method," getting students quickly communicating in the language. Rosalinda, an animated Aztec princess, is your teacher in these "engaging" and "clever" lessons focusing on daily activities, like shopping, as well as grammar skills, vocabulary, history and culture of Latin America. Video is excellent, content is excellent, in fact, *Estupendo!* for the entire CD.

BERLITZ THINK AND TALK FRENCH
– – – 15

$$$$$

HyperGlot Software Company, Inc.   Win/Mac
Language/French

Seven discs with 50 scenes are included in this "basic" series, which "comprehensively" leads users from simple hellos through full conversations. If you're a slow learner, these might be just the ticket; they drill over and over, testing reading, writing, and speaking skills. But if you're interested in multimedia bang for the buck, HyperGlot's Hyperlinks fail the test. These are no more than flash cards with some sound and a few pictures. The basic material is certainly covered, but as for CD flair: you might as well buy a book.

BERLITZ THINK AND TALK GERMAN
– – – 13

$$$$$

HyperGlot Software Company, Inc.   Win/Mac
Language/German
See *Berlitz Think and Talk French.*

BERLITZ THINK AND TALK ITALIAN
– – – 13

$$$$$

HyperGlot Software Company, Inc.   Win/Mac
Language/Italian
See *Berlitz Think and Talk French.*

BERLITZ THINK AND TALK SPANISH
15 15 14 **15**

$$$$$

HyperGlot Software Company, Inc.   Win/Mac
Language/Spanish
See *Berlitz Think and Talk French.*

BERNARD OF HOLLYWOOD'S MARILYN   11 14 16 **11**
$

Corel Corporation   Win/Mac
Current Affairs
Even the smallest screens sizzle in this multimedia journey through Marilyn Monroe's lifetime. Fans will enjoy this homage to the star, but there's nothing new here. Divided into strange essays and a timeline based on her relationship with photographer Bruno Bernard, the scarce videos consist of grainy news clips concentrating on her death. With a captivating interface and eye-catching graphics, Marilyn the screen star glows; yet, as always, the woman remains elusive.

BETTER HOMES AND GARDENS   16 20 12 **14**
COMPLETE GUIDE TO GARDENING
$$

Multicom Publishing, Inc.   Win/Mac
House and Garden
Green-thumbers with a flair for flora will enjoy this brilliantly-colored visit to annual, perennial, herb, wildflower and other gardens. There are brief instructional video clips and soothing music-to-plant-by accompanying a "helpful" reference guide with fundamentals and monthly tips. The index provides plant info from achimenes to zinnia, and matches flora colors, sizes and geographical zones. "Perfect" for many beginning gardeners, but some recommend buying the book it's based on.

BETTER HOMES AND GARDENS   – – – **15**
HEALTHY COOKING CD COOKBOOK
$$

Multicom Publishing, Inc.   Win/Mac
Cooking & Food
Based on *The New Dieter's Cookbook*, this CD has over 425 clearly presented recipes, all under 400 calories per serving. The title has many "useful" features, but is especially heavy on nutrition functions, such as the ability to find Sweet & Sour Ham Balls—the title's only low fat, low-cholesterol, 300 calorie dish containing veal. Eighty short, "functional," sometimes helpful videos illustrate basic techniques, but who needs to see how to use a garlic press?

BETTER PHOTOGRAPHY: – – – **19**
LEARNING TO SEE CREATIVELY
$$

DiAMAR Interactive Corporation   Win/Mac
Photography
Budding shutterbugs will find this program a patient teacher of the elements of line, design and light as well as the basics of camera use, from aperture to shutter speeds. It's especially fun to alter existing photos in the disc's database, and see how different techniques give style to snapshots. Information on darkroom techniques is noticeably missing. Still, *Better Photography* is a useful tool for improving camera craft.

BEYOND THE SAMBATYON: THE MYTH OF THE TEN LOST TRIBES

18 19 15 **18**
$

Creative Multimedia Corporation Win/Mac
History

Stacy Keach, television's *Mike Hammer*, narrates this intriguing quest into the fate of the Ten Lost Tribes of Israel after the Diaspora. Highlighted by its "good use" of superior graphics, real photographs, historical artifacts, ancient engravings and etchings, this title has users exploring history, playing archaeologist and anthropologist. Complete with international music, this disc is for "anyone interested in digging up historical and religious oddities."

BIG ANTHONY'S MIXED-UP MAGIC

17 20 16 **17**
Ages: 3-10 $

Putnam New Media Win/Mac
Kids/Stories

Consisting of an eight-chapter story by Tomie DePaola as well as 10 games and puzzles, this CD wins praise for its humor, "entertaining" music, and "beautiful animation." Engaging activities include memory games, a magic trick section, a musical improvisation section, as well as figuring out ingredients for magical cures to such ailments as headaches and warts. Not educational in the traditional sense, it does inspire "creative thinking," an important skill for young technophiles.

BIG BUG ALPHABET BOOK

- - - **12**
Ages: 3-8 $$

Milliken Publishing Co Win/Mac
Kids/Edugames-Spelling

Animated demonstrations that show how shapes combine to form letters are the heart of this alphabet story. With good graphics, clever transformations of bugs into letters and letters into other letters teach recognition in "an entertaining way." However, it's "not very interactive," contains long uninterruptible sequences, and the four included activities are "limited." Educationally sound, this is good for letter oriented toddlers and older ones having trouble with the alphabet.

BIG GREEN DISC

- - - **13**
$

Media Design Interactive Win/Mac
Science/General

Four areas cover environmental problems, solutions, organizations and discussion with various experts. A "polished" interface links information in the various sections which are enhanced with "gorgeous" photos and "compelling" videos. But this CD isn't as thorough as could be: endangered species are given "surprisingly limited" coverage and there's a lack of data sourcing and information substantiation. Still, with a section teaching ecology to kids, *Big Green* has inspiring moments.

BILL JAMES ELECTRONIC BASEBALL ENCYCLOPEDIA

– – – 18
$$

Miller Associates Win
Sports Reference

Every player who's ever stepped into the batter's box or pitched an inning in the bigs is here, and with a wide variety of sorting and reporting features, the numbers can be shaken, stirred and poured into the ultimate statistical milkshake. The encyclopedia also interfaces seamlessly with *Baseball for Windows*, allowing users to create and play with any combination of players from Cap Anson to Cal Ripken, Jr.

BIOFORGE

19 22 16 **19**
Ages: 17 & up $$$

Origin Systems, Inc. DOS
Games/Action

You've become a cyborg, but you won't let that stop you from uncovering the plot that threatens to blow up the planet, will you? "Excellent graphics" and "strong plot" make this a compelling, testosterone-rich experience, but "the interface becomes tedious, switching from combat to non-combat modes." And learning how to plant a fist on the baddies is a maddening exercise in frustration. You'll need a top of the line PC.

BIT-BOT'S MATH VOYAGE

– – – 19
Ages: 5-8 $$

Sanctuary Woods Multimedia Corporation Win/Mac
Kids/Edugames-Math

An updated version of *Math Ace Jr.*, kids enter a "colorful" submarine and meet the "cute" robot guide, Bit-Bot. From the sub's bridge, Bit-Bot takes users to eight "neat" math activities that emphasize real-world concepts like time, money, counting and, at harder levels, multiplication. By mastering games, kids earn fish and treasures for their virtual aquarium. Four levels occupy kids of varying abilities, and entertaining graphics and "humorous" animations keep kids interested.

BIZARRE ADVENTURES OF WOODRUFF AND THE SCHNIBBLE

17 19 16 **17**
$$

Sierra On-Line, Inc. Win
Games/Role-playing & Interactive Fiction

Yes, this is a zany animated adventure game. Players guide Woodruff, a punk-haired character on a post-apocalyptic quest through a "nonsensical" world. Searching for Schnibble, a mythical being that will lead the Boozooks from enslavement by humans means solving puzzles that "range from ludicrously simple to maniacally difficult." With "excellent" cartoon graphics and "refreshing" humor, *Woodruff* is "sure to entertain you," but joking aside, use a Pentium.

BLACK BEAUTY

18 20 18 **17**

Ages: 8-13 $

Sound Source Interactive Win

Kids/Stories

"Relive the classics" with this and others of the MovieBook series. With abbreviated story text and clips from the Warner Bros. movie, this "good quality" production is enjoyable —"at first." Kids may make it a one-shot deal, saying they've "already read it." There is a picture puzzle to solve if kids choose to read the text themselves instead of the narrated version. More such activities and "more videos" would add needed staying power.

BLIND DATE

7 11 9 **7**

$$

Trimark Interactive Win/Mac

Games/Role-playing & Interactive Fiction

There's only "two hours' worth of play here," but you'll want to hit the uninstaller option—the best feature— sooner. In this so-called interactive date, your goal is to bed dream-date Sandi before she leaves in a huff. Check her mood ring for hints as you choose between inane and suggestive banter, but your choices and her responses "don't seem to have anything to do with each other." Take a cold shower instead.

BLOCKBUSTER VIDEO GUIDE TO MOVIES & VIDEOS

11 19 15 **14**

$

Creative Multimedia Corporation Win

Movies/Reference

Don't call us, we'll call you. This "really cool CD" has 21,000 film reviews, 5000 stills, 4000 biographies and 40 short clips packaged in a "beautiful interface" that lets you "search in tons of ways." Yes, it's cool, but it lacks depth. The interface is "awkward" and could use more cross-links, Reviews are "too short," and ratings and text don't always jibe. Maybe just a quibble, but is *Dumb and Dumber* really better than *Body Heat*?

BLOOD BOWL

16 16 16 **14**

$

MicroLeague Interactive Software DOS

Games/Sports Simulation

It is the year 2488, and an Orc soldier unearths a strange book describing an ancient ritual between two teams. So marks the beginning of *Blood Bowl*, a futuristic football game played with a collection of elves, witches and assorted vermin. The game is played in turns, like a chess match, and despite "clumsy mechanics and gameplay," the "great subject matter" and plenty of "good old-fashioned violence" will satisfy "war gamers and bloodthirsty sports fans."

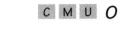

C M U O

BLOWN AWAY

17 21 16 **17**

$$
Win

IVI, Inc.
Games/Puzzle & Logic
Ever try the New York Times crossword, with a ticking bomb as your timer? This "fairly interesting" premise, based on the movie, has you racing against the clock to save your friends. The acting in the full-screen video clips is superior, and the game is "simple" to learn, but the difficulty of the varied puzzles is a mixed bag. In some cases, the solution depends less on logic and more on hand-eye coordination or just dumb luck.

BLUE & THE GRAY

– – – **10**

$
DOS

Impressions Software, Inc.
History/War
This title is a study guide for those unversed in the battles and leaders of the Civil War, and includes a Civil War strategy game as well. Top-notch armies are plagued with historically accurate problems and the results can go either way. But with a map interface that's confusing and help menus that are hard to find, the strategy game is difficult to play. Buy this title for the history; don't count on much interaction.

BOB DYLAN: HIGHWAY 61 INTERACTIVE

21 20 17 **19**

$$
Win/Mac

Graphix Zone
Music/Interactive Albums
A "rare, fully realized glimpse into one of the world's great artists" with dozens of music clips, videos, photos and facts—this is a comprehensive guide to Bob Dylan's life and work. But be prepared to spend time searching for all this information: the intentionally cryptic interface makes it feel "like you're locked in his house" rummaging "through his memorabilia." This experiential approach appeals to fans who say that "if you like Dylan, you'll love this CD."

BODY PARK

12 13 11 **14**

Ages: 4-10 $$
Win

Virtual Entertainment, Inc.
Kids/Edugames-Science
Picture a theme park, shaped like a human body—sort of EPCOT for budding doctors. Kids, along with a group of diverse friends, visit anatomy-based attractions featuring such topics as Nutrition, Heart, Brain and Muscles. Each area contains a game, a simple experiment to try off-PC, and elementary reference information. But *Body Park* is plagued with a "lack of interaction," and even "cheery music" doesn't save this "choppy" title from mixed reviews.

41

BODYWORKS 4.0

18 20 18 **18**

$$$

Softkey International   Win/Mac/DOS

Science/Anatomy

The human body is a beautiful, complex and intricate miracle of a machine. *BodyWorks 4.0* provides an "enjoyable" glimpse into that machine. The "graphics are excellent," with user-controlled 3-D viewers, videos and "very precise diagrams." Though users generally find that the content does not stand up to *A.D.A.M. The Inside Story*, this one is highly recommended for anybody interested in the body.

BOOKSHELF '95

22 22 23 **23**

$$$$

Microsoft Corporation   Win/Mac

Reference/Anthology

"Finding information is fast and easy" in this compendium of eight well-known references, including *Roget's Thesaurus, American Heritage Dictionary* and *Columbia* (not *Bartlett's*) *Dictionary of Quotations*. Most say it's elegant, with "everything a good reference library needs," but a few call it "superficial." The retooled 1995 version has new maps and 80,000 pronunciations. Great for locating out-of-reach little facts, but not for deep research.

BRETT HULL HOCKEY '95

17 15 16 **17**

$

Accolade, Inc.   DOS

Games/Sports Simulation

Hockey fans who prefer joysticks to skates may have a tough time finding their ice legs in this NHLPA licensed release. *Brett Hull* takes gamers close enough to taste shaved ice with large, fluid-looking skaters. Some applaud the "superior graphics and…exciting game play," while others call it a "limited view of the hockey experience." Roster management options are slim and printed reports are conspicuously absent. Action fans will enjoy the tough computer opponent.

BRIEF HISTORY OF TIME

22 13 16 **17**

See *Stephen Hawking's A Brief History of Time.*

BRITANNICA CD

19 6 10 **14**

$$$$$

Encyclopaedia Britannica Educational Corp   Win

Reference/Encyclopedias

If you want this "authoritative" encyclopedia, but haven't the shelf space for 32 books, get the disc. With 82,000 articles and "more than four times" the text of any other CD encyclopedia out there, *Brittanica* packs a wallop. The presentation has the *Brittanica* wheezy-barrister academic tone. With a "difficult" interface, dry content, and lack of multimedia, not to mention a price designed for sticker shock, you won't want this just to entertain the kids.

BUG ADVENTURE

19 19 19 **19**

Ages: 3-8 $

Knowledge Adventure   Win/DOS
Kids/Science

Watch a spider weave its web or a trap-door spider snag its prey. Images such as these—110 in all—and "captivating" information are presented in a "lively style" with an easy-to use interface. The "perfect indoor companion" to outdoor explorations, *Bug Adventure* has a complete Bug Reference, two good games, 3-D images and fascinating video clips. This "extraordinary" program "encourages investigation" of insects of all shapes and sizes.

BUREAU 13

14 16 8 **13**

$$

GameTek, Inc.   DOS
Games/Role-playing & Interactive Fiction

An "interesting story" and some "difficult puzzles" don't overcome the glitches in this race to subdue a rogue member of a secret government agency. Characters refuse to go where they're sent, others disappear for no reason, and items picked up and placed in inventory are suddenly back where they began. The 3-D graphics are "unimpressive," and the narration "barely understandable behind the music." An "A for effort," but it needs a lot of work.

BURIED IN TIME:
THE JOURNEYMAN PROJECT 2

20 22 20 **20**

$$$

Sanctuary Woods Multimedia Corporation   Win/Mac
Games/Role-playing & Interactive Fiction

Like its predecessor, this time-traveling adventure packs a wallop. "Awesome graphics" and "incredible animation," provide the backdrop for an "involved" and "interesting" plot. Once again you must travel in time, this time to the future, and use strategy and a quick trigger finger in order to avert disaster. With "very fast" game speed, and a user-friendly interface, this game will provide hours of fun for adventure and action game buffs alike.

BUSINESS PHONE '96

‒ ‒ ‒ **18**

$$

See *Pro CD Business Phone '96.*

BUSYTOWN

20 19 19 **18**

Ages: 3-7 $$

Viacom Interactive Media   Win/Mac/DOS
Kids/Edugames-General

This older title is based on the late Richard Scarry's popular *Busytown* books. Kids, accompanied by Huckle and other familiar book characters, tour the 12 activities of Busytown, lulled by a "soothing" musical score. The varied tasks include building a house by dragging parts to correct locations, helping the doctor bandage boo-boos on parts of the body, and visiting the firestation. Though a "favorite" for many, some tasks can be "difficult" for younger kids.

BUZZ ALDRIN'S RACE INTO SPACE

– – – 10

Ages: 13 & up $$$$

Interplay Productions   DOS
Science/Astronomy

Only serious space freaks will persist with this "not particularly well-designed" game that's "hard to get started with." The concept is great: a reconstructed Cold War race to the moon and there are 60 minutes of historic space program videos, but there's no real action to the game. It has "all the details" of the race to the moon, but "captures none of the glorious adventure."

CAMPAIGNS, CANDIDATES & THE PRESIDENCY

18 17 18 **18**

$

Compton's NewMedia   Win
History

From George Washington to Bill Clinton, the presidents and their campaigns are integral to American history. Opening the door to the Oval Office with a history of campaigns, this title covers all the major contenders to date, using timelines, articles and a presidential picture show. It features impressive multimedia, including audio and video, memorabilia from each executive, and a trivia game. It's a "good introduction," but if you're beyond that, "vote elsewhere."

CANADA PHONE

– – – 18

$$$$$

See *Pro CD Canada Phone*.

CANNON FODDER

16 16 19 **16**

$

Virgin Interactive Entertainment   DOS
Games/Combat

The name says it all. Almost a pure "shoot-'em-up," this "challenging little game" is an "addictive" and "fun diversion from the travails of life." Test your shooting reflexes as you steer a troop of soldiers, in "top down" view, through enemy territory—amassing soldiers by completing levels. After the "incredible intro," serious game enthusiasts may bemoan the "so-so" graphics, but even though not "super flashy," many find the game "very enjoyable."

CAR AND DRIVER '95 BUYER'S GUIDE

16 17 19 **16**

$

Sony ImageSoft   Win
Consumer Guides

"Packed" with tips for the "serious car buyer," yet "easy to use" even for novices, this title is more "educational" than visiting a dealer. It includes the standard offerings: ratings, features and prices, and goes somewhat beyond with on-line help and a technical glossary for the seriously confused. Also, there are "hundreds" of articles, photos and videos. The soundtrack can be "annoying," but sound buying advice makes this package "helpful."

CARDSHOP PLUS! DELUXE
21 20 20 **21**
$
Mindscape — Win
Graphics/Desktop Publishing

Here's one you won't want to discard. Now the whole family can enjoy making original greeting cards with this "fun to use" program. *CardShop* also outputs posters, certificates, banners and letterhead. The helpful Art Browser lets you scan a plentiful gallery of graphics, and a "great variety" of pithy salutations. For an economically-priced CD, "this one's a real bargain!"

CARMEN SANDIEGO TITLES
– – –

See *Where in the USA is Carmen Sandiego?, Where in the World is Carmen Sandiego?* and *Where in the World is Carmen Sandiego? Junior Detective Edition.*

CARTOON HISTORY OF THE UNIVERSE
21 21 21 **21**
$$
Putnam New Media — Win/Mac
Comics

An "irreverent" and "entertaining" adaptation of Larry Gonick's popular book, this two-disc set highlights events from the Big Bang through Alexander the Great's conquests in 330 BC. Wrapped in an "eye catching interface," are 2000 animations and five hours of "narrated stories" on everything from evolution to pyramid building. Seventeen short games, while not deep, are a "pleasant distraction." Perhaps a bit "sugar-coated," it's still a "pure delight" that provides thoughtful information.

CASPER BRAINY BOOK
– – – **19**
$$
Knowledge Adventure — Win/Mac
Kids/Stories

Join Casper, the friendly ghost, and his three uncles (Fatso, Stretch and Stinkie) in a playful romp through their house. Explore by clicking on various parts of the brightly colored screens. Objects come alive, ghosts fly about, and a narrator reads the story. Kids find hidden keys to play three games (jig-saw, spelling and concentration). A fun title—with good graphics and music.

CHAOS CONTROL
– – – **19**
$$
Philips Media Games — DOS
Games/Role-playing & Interactive Fiction

Beautifully rendered 3-D animations set the stage for an epic shoot-'em-up space adventure. The year is 2025 and a tribe of extraterrestrials, called the Kesh Rahn, are invading Manhattan island. As space ace Jessica Darkhill, you work your way through increasingly difficult levels of arcade style games in a quest to liberate Manhattan and destroy the nemesis Commander Arakh Kreen, leader of the Kesh Rahn. Play is addictive and pulse-quickening.

CHESSMASTER 4000 TURBO — — — 19

$$

Mindscape Win
Games/Parlor

Everything a chess player could want—except, of course, a human opponent. A "very good" chess player, it's powerful and easy-to-use, with bells and whistles galore. You can change boards, set playing times, level of play—even switch opponents mid-game. If you're in a pickle, you can find quick hints and detailed advice; "in a real jam— switch sides." Speed depends on your PC; less than a 386DX/40 and you and your computer are in time trouble.

CHUCK JONES' PETER AND THE WOLF 19 18 18 **18**

Ages: 3-8 $

Time-Warner Interactive Group Win/Mac
Kids/Music

Sergei Prokofiev's "classic" score is matched with "wonderful" animation by Bugs Bunny animator Jones in a "simple" disc that "inspires music appreciation." The "fun," "cute" story of Peter, who saves his meadow from the Wolf, was written to teach children about orchestra instruments—and the moods that can be created through melody. "It's even fun for adults," but limited interaction and a "lame" game means older siblings dismiss this "beautiful," "clever" composition as "boring!"

CHUGALONG GOES TO PLAYLAND 12 10 11 **11**

Ages: 3-6 $$

Maxis Win
Kids/Stories

Chugalong offers "educational value," but also some "serious flaws:" it's too slow, too "simple," too "repetitive," and worst of all, the 3-D animation is "bizarre" and "creepy." Kids can follow narration or head off on their own, learning letters, puzzles, even music—and the "easy to use" interactivity works well. However, it's got horror movie undertones: "screechy" voices and characters that look like "killer dolls." There is educational value—if kids aren't scared away first.

CINEMANIA '95 22 21 22 **21**

$$$

Microsoft Corporation Win/Mac
Movies/Reference

This exhaustive movie enthusiast's dream is centered around 20,000 one-paragraph reviews from Leonard Maltin's review book. "A must for film buffs," it includes film stills, original scores, dialogue, quotes and 21 video clips. The graphics are high quality, and the often familiar sounds are clear and crisp. Some users find the "interface a bit awkward," and would like a little "more multimedia content." Overall, however, this product is a box office hit.

CIRCUS

19 20 20 **20**

Ages: 6-12 $

Voyager Company   Win/Mac
Kids/Stories

This nostalgic romp through the big-top is great for kids of all ages. Comprised of a number of circus feats which children must actively help to complete, this title is "colorfully animated" and has an "appropriately simple" interface. The graphics are wonderful, and the music is "catchy." The activities range from firing a human cannonball to helping a lion "see-saw" a ball through a hoop. Like the circus itself, this title is full of surprises.

CLARK HOWARD'S CONSUMER SURVIVAL KIT

21 11 19 **19**

$$

IBM Multimedia Studio   Win
Consumer Guides

Consumer advocate Clark Howard teaches how to be a smart consumer, from the "big basics"—investments, insurance, and real estate—to the "small specifics," like "how to return a lemon." Whether buying a house or making everyday purchases, even careful consumers find they learn "a lot from this disc." With only black-and-white videos, it's not flashy and screens are "crowded," but it's a "great reference" for "big money decisions."

CLIFFS STUDYWARE FOR THE S.A.T. I

- - - **11**

$$

Cliffs Studyware   Win/Mac
Test Preparation

The study guides that helped you ace Shakespeare are a "disappointment" when it comes time to prep for the SAT. The practice tests and study drills are designed in such a way as to deliver a "clutter of windows" on your screen. The video doesn't "provide insight" into the test and the drills are "poorly designed." Some of the writing uses "poor style and grammar." Better to select one of the other test-prep programs readily available.

CLOCK WERX

19 18 18 **19**

$

Spectrum Holobyte, Inc.   Win/Mac
Games/Arcade

Action puzzle fans need "look no further" than *Clockwerx*. Users maneuver a clock hand towards a goal as the hand swings from dot-to-dot on a grid. As you progress through levels, new obstacles and "treacherous moving objects" are added in increasingly complex screens. Unlike many twitch games, this one "actually gets harder, rather than just faster." You'll need "acute deductive powers" and "impeccable" timing for this "torturously good" game.

CLUB DEAD

15 18 16 **16**

See *MTV's Club Dead.*

CNN NEWSROOM GLOBAL VIEW
14 12 14 **14**
$
Compact Publishing, Inc.   Win
Current Affairs

Using a "newsroom interface," video cameras zoom users off to six "newsworthy" topics, covering the people, politics, resources and military of various "hot spot" countries. An atlas attempts to underscore current events with information on the places they occur. But video is "jerky" and the news and atlas information is out-of-date. The fun World Clock graphically shows how seasons affect daylight hours around the world, but isn't enough to carry this CD.

COLONIZATION
20 13 16 **19**
$$$
MicroProse Software, Inc.   Mac/DOS
Games/Simulation

A refreshing change from zapping aliens, but "not a whole lot different" from the immensely popular *Civilization*, except the timeframe here is "limited to about 300 years" instead of 10,000. The "click-and-drag mouse controls" take some "time getting used to" and the miniature graphics can be challenging to decipher (stockades look like teepees), but the soundtrack's appropriate drum-and-fife, banjo and fiddle tunes are a real pleaser.

COMANCHE CD
16 22 19 **20**
$$$
Nova Logic, Inc.   DOS
Games/Combat

The ride in an RAH-66 Comanche is awesome as it zips along the ground flying over boulders and rivers. But it only zips if you've got enough memory, which usually means "using a boot disk." Otherwise, the slo-mo ride is like flying through marshmallows. Not only is this an "excitingly realistic" flight simulator, but also a "good game," with training missions and operations galore that lead up to the ultimate theater-wide campaign.

COMIC BOOK CONFIDENTIAL
19 19 19 **19**
$$
Voyager Company   Win/Mac
Art Appreciation

Take the 90-minute Ron Mann *Comic Book Confidential* documentary, a fascinating history of comic books, add "a pile of interesting" material—and you've got this title. Interesting bits include the text of the McCarthy-era Comic Book Code, a self-censorship standard adopted by the comics industry. Learn about such artists as Frank Miller, R. Crumb and Stan Lee. Though "not comprehensive," it's a "fresh and interesting" picture of the "forbidden pleasures" of the comic world.

COMMAND AND CONQUER

– – –

$$$
Virgin Interactive Entertainment
DOS
Games/Combat

From the folks who brought you the award-winning *DUNE II*, this futuristic strategy game offers you the choice of being one of the Good Guys or the Bad, and lets you face off against friends using modem or network play. Build bases and manufacturing facilities, mine for Tiberium minerals and defend your territory in 35-plus missions. Sounds like a big game, and it is; it takes two CDs to contain it all.

COMPLETE BASEBALL '95

22 19 20 **21**

$$
Microsoft Corporation
Win
Sports Reference

If bigger is better, you'll love this macrocoverage sports/trivia reference, crammed with juicy statistics, biographies, dates, facts and photos. Some users call it a "rip-off," loaded with great facts but "almost no video." Others are annoyed that it's a "buck-and-a-quarter a day" to use the online update feature. But it's packed with "a zillion stats," a mind-bending quiz, and a nostalgic trip through baseball memorabilia, making it a thrill for any true fan.

COMPLETE MAUS

21 15 15 **18**

$$
Voyager Company
Mac
Comics

Art Spiegelman's famous two-volume *Maus*, the comic-format story of his father's Holocaust experience, is here in its entirety. There are conversations with Spiegelman, preliminary sketches, and taped interviews with his father (including a 706-page transcript). Spiegelman admits the story, having been designed for a vertical page, doesn't look as good on screen. But guided by his "measured, soft spoken" voice, the "moving" interviews, sketches and story itself, add up to a worthwhile "extension" of the books.

COMPLETE MULTIMEDIA BIBLE

18 18 17 **18**

$$
Compton's NewMedia
Win
Religion

Sunday school was never this engrossing. James Earl Jones narrates this "rich mix of sound, video and text," set in a glossy interface that presents the world's most examined text in a new light. You can read and explore each book of the King James Bible, enriched with study guides and quizzes. A "well-written" history of the Bible is a tacked-on bonus, though it's "troubling" that no source for this material is given.

COMPLETE NBA BASKETBALL

21 20 19 **20**
$$

Microsoft Corporation Win
Sports Reference

This slam-dunk title succeeds in reconstructing the excitement of pivotal moments in basketball history. The no-nonsense interface allows you to get right to the information you're seeking, or just browse the entertaining text and interviews with the greats. Dribble, cheer and swish sound effects add to the fun. Get updates through a daily on-line newspaper, "though this can get expensive." This title will appeal to sports fans looking to share their enthusiasm with the basketball-unschooled.

COMPOSER COLLECTION

20 21 22 **20**
$$$

Microsoft Corporation Win
Music/Appreciation

These three entrees in the Microsoft Home series introduce users to the world of classical music. With a comfortable interface and "wonderful" audio, these titles analyze and explain three works by three of the world's most renowned composers: Beethoven's *Ninth Symphony*, Mozart's *Dissonant Quartet* and Schubert's *Trout Quintet*. Although each title is limited to discussion of a single work, most users found they provide "excellent insight" and are a "pleasure to use."

COMPTON'S ENCYCLOPEDIA OF AMERICAN HISTORY

18 16 15 **19**
$$

Compton's NewMedia Win
History

If content were everything, this CD would be rated numero uno. Students of history, both learned and not, can access a lot from this program. Information is "good" and "up-to-date" covering all major and "many minor" points of American History. Unfortunately, "excellent" content, based on a highly-rated college textbook, doesn't quite make up for a "cluttered" and "buggy" interface. The messy screens "detracted" from the fun, so use it in a scholarly, not super-duper-multimedia-lovin', way.

COMPTON'S INTERACTIVE ENCYCLOPEDIA 1994 AND 1995 EDITIONS

19 18 18 **19**
$$$

Compton's NewMedia Win/Mac
Reference/Encyclopedias

"Perfectly designed for exploration," *Compton's* lets you ask questions in natural language. If you ask "why is the sky blue?," for example, you'll retrieve a list of about 200 related articles. More traditional search tools include an alphabetical index, a timeline, and a "topic tree." Kids enjoy creating presentations in the "editing room," using *Compton's* good multimedia content. The biggest criticism? Some call the articles "shallow." All say the 1995 version is dramatically "improved over earlier versions."

C M U *O*

CONGO: THE MOVIE—DESCENT INTO ZINJ
- - -
$$$

Viacom Interactive Media Win/Mac
Games/Role-playing & Interactive Fiction
Rule of thumb—if the movie flops, cover your losses else-where. This one sends you in search of characters from the Michael Crichton novel and the film, who got lost in their quest for a huge diamond cache. Using a first-person per-spective, players are geared with high-tech equipment to defend themselves against jungle beasts, hostile natives, as well as earthquakes, landslides and volcanic eruptions—a sort of '*Doom* Goes To Africa.'

CONSUMER REPORTS CARS: THE ESSENTIAL GUIDE
- - -
$

Creative Multimedia Corporation Win
Consumer Guides
Using Consumer Reports information, this disc rates over 2,000 new and used cars from 1987 to 1996. The search tool that helps find cars for your needs and budgets sounds promising, as does the video on evaluating a used car. But the Interactive Video Negotiation, for learning to deal with salespeople seems gimmicky. There's a fee-based online link for information updates. It's likely a worthwhile disc, even with all the Consumer Reports self-promotion it contains.

CONSUMER SURVIVAL KIT
21 11 19 **19**

See *Clark Howard's Consumer Survival Kit.*

CORAL REEF! THE VANISHING UNDERSEA WORLD
17 19 17 **18**
Ages: 6 & up $

Arnowitz Studios Win/Mac
Science/Animals
Coral reefs are nature's art galleries and this "beautiful, thorough (though academic) reference tool" with an "envi-ronmental" slant, lets you explore their beauty and hidden life in "fascinating detail." The disc feels "close" to being there, with "stunning" videos and photos, excellent nar-ration and "lots of info." Before diving in, note that it's "slow," and the text searching is "mediocre." Still, an engrossing and attractive disc with "plenty of heart."

COUNTING ON FRANK
17 16 17 **16**
Ages: 8-11 $$

Creative Wonders Win/Mac
Kids/Edugames-Math
If Henry (Frank's his dog) guesses the number of jelly-beans in the jar, he goes to Hawaii, and kids solve math word-problems to help him. Colorful pictures and cute skits keep 'em giggling, and the math game is "enjoyable." But the design is awkward—"too slow between scenes," "confusing" and there are "not enough buzzers, flashing lights, or action." Finally, only three difficulty levels may mean a prematurely retired title.

CRAYOLA AMAZING ART ADVENTURE

19 20 19 19

Ages: 3-6 $$

Micrografx   Win

Kids/Art & Writing

This coloring program lets budding artists create pictures worthy of showings in only the finest of refrigerator galleries. *Art Adventure* has some "fun, good features," including coloring books and dot-to-dot games. The drawing tools that make this program "unique" include talking letters, crazy graphics, magical effects that smear and swirl, and 60 animated stickers that bring pictures to life. A good choice for less-than-perfectionist pre-schoolers: it's hard to stay in the lines.

CRAYOLA ART STUDIO

17 16 19 17

Ages: 3-6 $$

Micrografx   Win

Kids/Art & Writing

Create a certificate for Mom or Dad—just for being smart enough to buy this program! Though "not as good as *Kid-Pix*," this drawing package is filled with things to "keep kids occupied for hours." Coloring books, draw-by-numbers, and various other activities are presented in an easy-to-use, colorful package. Wacky sound effects keep children from getting bored, while the graphics are just off-the-wall enough to make every creation, well, um… unique!

CREATE YOUR DREAM JOB

- - - 17

$$

Wilson Learning Corporation   Win/Mac

Personal Development

Learn the four key steps to career happiness by examining your talents, passion, vision and ideal environment. Do this by meeting and advising fictional characters at different career impasses. The presentation is extremely linear, but there have never been any short cuts to discovering your dream job. Video is over-used in this CD-with-a-distinctly-corporate-training-style. However, it's a patient and thorough electronic counselor for anyone suffering from general career malaise.

CREATIVE WRITER

19 21 19 19

Ages: 8-14 $$

Microsoft Corporation   Win/Mac

Kids/Art & Writing

It's good to get kids' creative juices flowing early and this "very inspirational" product helps do just that. Children are guided through the story creation process, with helpful hints on plot, writing, ideas, style and graphics. The main program component is a simple word processor, but the surrounding accessories make it worthwhile. A "great first writing program" despite (or for kids, maybe because of) "annoying sounds" and a "juvenile" interface, it encourages "much experimenting."

CREATURE SHOCK

12 22 13 **15**

$$

Virgin Interactive Entertainment
DOS
Games/Combat

Beyond the fancy-shmancy intro lies a reworking of the *Alien* film plot—edge your way through the space ship and be ready to blast slimy, buggy creatures at every turn. Then it's on to the outpost and—you guessed it—blasting more slimy, buggy creatures. Some think it's "a nice mix of arcade and adventure," but despite the "cool 3-D eye-catching graphics" and the "initial excitement," more users complain the game "becomes boring real fast."

CRUNCHER

- - - **18**

Ages: 10 & up $$

Davidson & Associates, Inc.

Win/Mac
Kids/Edugames-Math

So you're managing a small lemonade stand, and you need to calculate rising costs (sugar) versus declining sales (rain). Welcome to *Cruncher*, the "combination educational spreadsheet and business application" for kids. With fun examples, games and tutors, including a crazy sax-playing dude, kids learn to use a spreadsheet program just like Mom's and Dad's. It's "creative and easy to use," though it takes time to learn. Expect to spend time helping your young entrepreneur.

CYBERBOOGIE! WITH SHARON, LOIS & BRAM

14 19 13 **14**

Ages: 3-9 $$

Times Mirror Multimedia
Win/Mac
Kids/Music

Sharon, Lois and Bram don't stick around long, but this tuneful title doesn't need the popular singers to keep kids absorbed. Cute and peppy, *Cyberboogie!* gets kids making musical puppet shows, though "too few animation tools" limits the life of this activity. The "funny" characters bop to the beat, with animated movement and dancing. Younger kids "danced to it," boogying down to "great songs" like "Eensy Weensy Spider," but kids lose interest "after the first hour."

CYBERIA

16 18 19 **16**

$$$

Interplay Productions
DOS
Games/Combat

An "uneven" but good grab bag with a "bit of something for everyone." Select an emphasis on arcade action, "aim your sights and blast away" (although experienced gamers may be "disappointed"), or set the difficulty level and try to solve an "inconsistent collection" of puzzles. "Fantastic" graphics and an orchestral soundtrack accompany Zak Kingston, a felon who must penetrate the Cyberia complex or be sent back to the slammer. Nice "auto save" feature takes the worry out of being creamed.

CYBERWAR

14 18 11 **13**

$$

Sales Curve Interactive
Mac/DOS
Games/Combat
It takes three discs (and a bonus audio CD) to retell the story of *The Lawnmower Man*. If you never saw the movie, you may be confused by Dr. Angelo's surreal struggle against his virtual nemesis, Cyberjobe. While there are a dozen puzzles or arcade events to surmount, there's "not enough playability." Lush graphics abound, but if you "just want to sit and stare at a screen, might as well watch TV." It's cheaper.

CYCLEMANIA

– – – **16**

$$$

Accolade, Inc.
DOS
Games/Sports Simulation
The action is on the track in this fast-moving, arcade-style road racing game. The innovative use of real-life road and background videos, coupled with animated hazards, provide a realistically paced environment, even on a double speed drive. However, a lack of mechanical options—you can't tinker with your bike—limits solo playing appeal. Still, the need for speed can be satiated here, and the two-player modem option is a fast ride all the way.

D!ZONE COLLECTORS EDITION

18 17 14 **17**

Ages: 13 & up $

WizardWorks, Inc.
DOS
Games/Action
So you've just finished *Doom II*, your fingers are still twitching and you've got no one to blast with your plasma rifle, eh? You need *D!Zone*, a compilation of hints, help files, graphics and sound editors, and—get this—another 900 or so levels. Some are super, some are "stupid," and some don't work, period. There's "enough battleground to last until hell freezes over." You'll need a registered copy of *Doom* or *Doom II* first.

DAEDALUS ENCOUNTER

17 22 18 **19**

$$$

Virgin Interactive Entertainment
Win/Mac
Games/Role-playing & Interactive Fiction
Adventuring with a tightly leather-clad Tia Carrere—what could possibly be better? Unfortunately, you are merely a human brain with a computer life-support system, so schmoozing with this space cadet is not on your agenda. *Daedalus* sports "incredible" graphics, an "impressive" interface and an "interesting plot." Unfortunately, some found that the "limited" interaction curbed their enjoyment of this big-budget production, while others longed for a way to view the entire movie "without solving those annoying puzzles."

DANGEROUS CREATURES

23 22 23 **22**

Ages: 8 & up $$

Microsoft Corporation   Win/Mac

Science/Animals

This nature disc is unique in that it appeals to both "the young, non-reading animal lover, and the older serious science student." It's an "entertaining and interesting" visual feast of art, photography and "very good videos—lots of them." Explore the content with 12 different tour guides, from an African storyteller to a wildlife photographer. Pronunciations are provided for many words. This disc goes beyond glitz to provide an "educational" experience for all.

DARK EYE

– – –

$$$

iNscape   Win/Mac

Games/Role-playing & Interactive Fiction

Looking for weird? Here's weird. William Burroughs, renowned author of *Naked Lunch*, provides the narration for this exploration of the mind of Edgar Allan Poe. By using a phrenologist's cranial map, you move through the nightmare world of three Poe-inspired stories, all illustrated by the stop-motion graphics of *Beetlejuice* animator Doug Beswick and accompanied by the beat of electronic music guru Thomas Dolby. Sounds intriguing but not one for the kids.

DARK FORCES

23 23 22 **23**

$$$

LucasArts Entertainment Co.   Mac/DOS

Games/Combat

Ready. Set. Shoot lots of bad guys. Part of a series based on the *Star Wars* saga, this latest installment might lack originality, but scores with the fast, 3-D, *Doom*-style interface. There are great weapons, familiar adversaries (Jabba The Hut), and besides shooting, you need to solve some tricky puzzles to advance. A "great concept" with "all the action, but half the gore" of *Doom*.

DAZZELOIDS

14 18 19 **15**

Ages: 7 & up $

Voyager Company   Win/Mac

Kids/Stories

This mixed bag children's CD disappoints. Loosely constructed around the cartoon *Dazzeloids*, complete with biography of these mythical characters, the Dazzeloids' mission is to wipe out boredom. But with its limited interaction, the boredom is transferred to your home instead, as kids wind up mostly watching the three short, "threadbare" stories. One thing in ample supply is "bathroom humor." Otherwise, this "unruly" title fails to dazzle.

DEAD SEA SCROLLS REVEALED
21 18 15 **16**
$$

Logos Research Systems Win/Mac
History

Discovered in a cave in 1947, the Dead Sea Scrolls have lately piqued popular interest. Using video, music and text, this title delves into the ancient mystery and modern intrigue of these parchment fragments. But the inspired art design doesn't mask the "clumsy" and "unintuitive" interface. And despite the "impressive" depth of content and intelligent links, the dry presentation doesn't invite repeat viewings. Still, there's lot's of history here for those with an interest in religious studies or archaeology.

DEAL-A-MEAL INTERACTIVE (RICHARD SIMMONS)
– – – **15**
$$$

GT Interactive Software DOS
Cooking & Food

The energetic exercise and diet guru comes to life on CD. Packed with diet recipes and exercise tips, the disc helps you create a personalized weight-loss program, although its main message is motivation. Video clips of Simmons are interspersed with inspirational quotes and nutrition and exercise pointers, and the disc comes with the Deal-A-Meal color-coded cards and wallet. "As corny as the TV program" but an "encouraging" and "helpful" way to start a weight-loss program.

DESCENT
21 22 21 **22**
$$

Interplay Productions DOS
Games/Combat

This "excellent" "shoot-em-up" game is "hard to beat." Building on *Doom's* interface, this "awesome" package allows players to maneuver their mining vehicle 360 degrees, in a 3-D environment, to seek out and eliminate a variety of enemy machines. "Incredible graphics and animation" are "fast," and make this title a "heart-pounding experience." Maneuvering your ship takes a while to perfect, but true fans of quick-moving search-and-destroy games will be "thrilled."

DIG
– – –
$$$

LucasArts Entertainment Co. Mac/DOS
Games/Role-playing & Interactive Fiction

When Steven Spielberg affixes his name to a computer game, it sure creates a buzz. Here, he has "inspired" (whatever that means) a deep-space adventure about a team of explorers stranded on an alien planet. Doesn't sound unusual, but you can bet when Industrial Light & Magic generates the special effects, it'll be something to see. The book, audio drama, and audio CD will be released simultaneously. That's called heavy marketing, folks.

DIGGERS

16 8 10 **12**

$$

Millennium Media Group, Inc.   Win/DOS

Games/Puzzle & Logic

Meet a poor cousin to the *Lemmings* series. While billed as a fast-paced game, it is anything but. Control tiny creatures as they burrow their way past a variety of hazards towards subterranean riches. This is a "mindless, practically tranquilizing," yet "addictive diversion." There are no clues as to where the gems are buried, making it necessary to wander back and forth over the huge playing field hoping to stumble on some valuable rocks.

DINOSAURS!

23 21 21 **22**

$$

Microsoft Corporation   Win/Mac

Science/Dinosaurs

Dinosaurs! goes to "the head of the class" in "multimedia learning." With a "good overview" of the "major types of dinosaurs," this "interesting information" is accompanied by picture galleries and slide shows. Exploration is easy, as users search by name, family, continent or time period. The six movies are "mostly narrated animation sequences." Rising above the "plethora" of pre-historic titles, this is sure to satisfy your curiosity about the life and times of T. Rex.

DIRECT PHONE

21 – 20 **20**

$$$$

Pro CD, Inc.   Win/Mac/DOS

Phone Directories

Discontinued and replaced by *Home & Business Phone '96*. For more information, see review of *Pro CD Phone Books* series.

DISCOVERIES: SKY HIGH

– – – **18**

D.C. Heath and Co.   Win/Mac

Kids/Science

The history of flight along with facts and stories about the planets and the atmosphere are presented in this grade school title. Kids explore a 360 degree panorama, with a corresponding timeline and hot buttons, or by topic, to get to videos and short text on such topics as Saturn, a Wright Brothers plane, or Amelia Earhart. The program is slow and a bit cumbersome, but has nice graphics and good content. It comes with a journal and ideas to stimulate kids' writing, making this a good in-school title.

DISCOVERING SHAKESPEARE

- - - 17
$

IVI, Inc. Win/Mac
Literature
This disc weaves together historical notes, documentary video clips, and period maps and drawings to detail the life, times and works of England's greatest Bard. The interface is simple, and the background music gets repetitive, but there are useful act-by-act play summaries and vignettes about Shakespeare's life and times. The Legends section discusses the controversy surrounding Shakespeare's real identity.

DISCWORLD

21 19 21 21
$$

Psygnosis, Ltd. DOS
Games/Role-playing & Interactive Fiction
Can a not-too-clever wizard rid Ankh-Morpork of a dragon before getting kicked out of wizard university? Only if you teach him the skills to do so. This "absolutely hysterical" quirky adventure, based on Terry Pratchett's 21-plus book series, has a few sound bugs in it that affect the narration by Monty Python's Eric Idle. But a combination of terrific artwork, entertaining story and challenging puzzles make this very long game "highly enjoyable."

DISTANT SUNS: DESKTOP PLANETARIUM

19 15 18 17
Ages: 14 & up $$$

Virtual Reality Laboratories, Inc. Win/Mac
Science/Astronomy
With *Distant Suns*, you can orient yourself precisely in a 3-D recreated celestial environment and study the position and movement of all the galactic bodies on any given day, past or future. The tools to do this, however, are rather technical and assume previous astronomical knowledge. Besides flash cards that challenge the user's knowledge of the constellations, the program is "a bit weak on entertainment." Given the heavy use of astro-lingo, this title is for serious star-gazers only.

DOCTOR'S BOOK OF HOME REMEDIES

14 7 14 13
$

Compton's NewMedia Win/Mac/DOS
Medical Reference
A disc incarnation of the Rodale Press book that "strikes a good balance" between traditional and alternative medicine therapies on conditions ranging from allergies to wrinkles. The disc has the full text of the book, but "doesn't offer much more." There are no photographs and multimedia is scarce, with 15 short, "superficial" videos on conditions like snoring and back pain. The "personal health check-up" gives pretty generic feedback. Buy the book instead.

DOGS

Microsoft Corporation

$$ ·· Win

Pets

Dogs looks and feels a lot like "Dorling Kindersley's general science books." Conventional menus and doggie guide characters walk you through. There's "useful information" about choosing breeds, training, and ownership and some amusing "stupid pet trick" videos and trivia quizzes. But poor hyper-links often lead you to brief definitions rather than the full section on a subject, and there's no information on canine inoculations, leaving not much meat "for a serious dog lover."

DOOM HEAVEN

Most Significant Bits

$ ·· DOS

Games/Combat

Well, it's definitely heaven… for hard-core *Doom* fans, anyway. There's an "obscene" number of new screens, scenarios, plots, monsters, guns and pretty much anything else a *Doom*-aphile can think of. The program even has its own, very convenient interface which allows you to examine the add-ons before actually loading them into the game. *Doom Heaven* requires installation of either *Doom* or *Doom II*.

DOOM II: HELL ON EARTH

GT Interactive Software

$$$ ·· Mac/DOS

Games/Combat

"Truly Awesome!" "Violent," "fast," "destructive." This "outstanding" game gives players a variety of weapons to annihilate busloads of evil creatures. The *Doom* interface, which lets users race through a non-stop multi-level labyrinth at top speed, practically defined a game genre. Don't expect major differences from the shareware version, though you do get some new levels. Due to wanton "violence," you may want to "keep it away from kids."

DR. HEALTH'NSTEIN'S BODY FUN

StarPress Multimedia

Ages: 8 & up $
Win/Mac

Kids/Science

Understanding healthy eating and appropriate exercise is necessary in life, as it is in this game about healthy living. Dividing life into four stages, kids gather points and meet the physical challenges needed to move to the next level. There's "good content," that's "age appropriate" and kids learn the right way—by doing . But despite "a great concept," "choices are few" and the text is "dull," limiting the longevity of the title.

DR. RUTH'S ENCYCLOPEDIA OF SEX 19 17 19 **19**

$
Creative Multimedia Corporation   Win
Science/Anatomy

The little grandmother is at it again—giving young people advice about their sex life, this time interactively. This "completely unerotic" title contains over 250 entries about diseases, self-examinations, pregnancy and a range of other topics. Complete with video clips, Dr. Ruth's characteristic voice, over 800 high-quality graphics, and a "pleasant" and "simple" interface, this title entertains as it educates. If you want a disc that is both "tasteful" and "frank," consult Dr. Ruth. *This title is included in the 5 ft. 10 Pak Collector's Edition.*

DR. SCHEULER PRESENTS THE CORNER DRUGSTORE – – –

$$$
Pixel Perfect Software   Win
Medical Reference

Considering a glass of burgundy with that Benadryl? First check *The Corner Drug Store*. This four-disc title contains information on more than 8,000 medications. The InteRact feature gives users a chance to analyze the potential side effects of various drug combinations. The interface, much like that of the other Dr. Scheuler's titles, is not exactly warm and inviting, but contains a truckload of helpful data, including more than five hours of video clips.

DR. SCHUELER'S HOME MEDICAL ADVISOR PRO, VERSION 4.0 19 18 18 **19**

$$$
Pixel Perfect Software   Win
Medical Reference

Click on a picture of your problem area, or type in symptoms to bring up a list of potential ailments. Then brace yourself: the list may be long, and may include some rare and unlikely illnesses. Also, "surprisingly gruesome photos" are not for those whose symptoms include a weak stomach. But 1200 color photos and 100 videos illustrate information on over 800 diseases, 200 injuries, 500 household poisons and 5000 drugs, making this "a solid multimedia reference work."

DR. SCHUELER'S SELF HEALTH 18 15 20 **18**

$$
Pixel Perfect Software   Win
Medical Reference

Create health profiles for family members that include physical and psychological make-up, health records and family histories. The program then assesses each person's risk of major ailments like heart disease. The "emphasis" is "on preventive care," with such narrated video clips as a breast self-exam. An "extensive" list of organizations that provide information on diseases and treatments is included. Though some say it lacks "detail," the sound advice is "good for peace of mind."

DR. SEUSS'S ABC

– – – 23

Ages: 3-7 $$
Living Books Win/Mac
Kids/Edugames-Reading

If only Dr. Seuss were around to see this remarkably grace-ful leap to CD-ROM. The animations and audio that are added are faithful to the style and spirit of Seuss's ABC book, enhancing without overwhelming the original. Like all the other Living Books, there's plenty of clickable animations and words are highlighted as they're read. Already interactive in book form, it's a perfect vehicle for a multimedia conversion—now *Dr. Seuss's ABC* is more engaging than ever.

DR. T'S SING-A-LONG AROUND THE WORLD

19 21 21 20

Ages: 3-10 $
Dr. T's Music Software Win
Kids/Music

This "MTV for preschoolers" is short on education, but the musical exposure is still there. You'll hear children's songs from around the world, in their native languages and in English, played and illustrated "in slide show fashion," with follow-along lyrics and notes. You can adjust song speed, eliminate lyrics, or get a microphone and sing-along karaoke-style. While the disc "could use more songs," the audio quality is high, and it's "fun to use and watch."

DR. T'S SING-A-LONG KIDS CLASSICS

18 17 20 17

Ages: 3-10 $
Dr. T's Music Software Win
Kids/Music

The forerunner to *Dr. T's Sing-A-Long Around the World*, this title features a kids' menu that's "easy to use, but hard to get to." Illustrative icons make choosing songs enticing. Animation, "great CD sound" and scrolling follow-along words make this a fun way for kids to hear their favorite vocal classics. "My daughter reliably asks for it once a month." It's good reading practice, too…but like its sequel, it isn't karaoke unless you provide a microphone.

DRACULA UNLEASHED

16 19 18 18

$
Viacom Interactive Media Mac/DOS
Games/Role-playing & Interactive Fiction

From Bram Stoker's popular myth, this "dynamic," "diffi-cult" "great interactive movie" puts you in vampire-haunted Victorian England. By choosing various actions, you activate filmed scenes, leading to further choices. There are plenty of red herrings, and the order in which you do things matters, so count on "lots of trial and error" to avoid becoming vampire grub. True vampirephiles lament this "PG-13" film's lack of "gory details," but it's still worth a bite.

DRAGON LORE: CODE OF THE DRAGON KNIGHTS

18 21 17 **18**
$$

Mindscape DOS

Games/Role-playing & Interactive Fiction

In this two-disc medieval fantasy adventure, you become a warrior attempting the rank of Dragon Knight through combat and by solving challenging ("Help! I'm stuck—I need to buy the hint book") puzzles. With each click of the mouse, your view changes. Expect "long stretches of puzzle-solving and exploration" with sporadic bouts of "fast-paced action." Its "stunning graphics" with "fluid 3-D" animations and "well-balanced" puzzles are game highlights.

EA* KIDS ART CENTER

19 20 19 **17**

Ages: 3 & up $$

Creative Wonders Win/Mac

Kids/Art & Writing

Five activity areas offer a rainbow of creative opportunities for artistic expression and manipulative learning, from a structured Coloring Book to a free-form Paint Box. Block Art lets kids create original or blueprint designs. In Costumes, they play dress-up with clickable attire and cartoon people. Designed so that "even very young children can create right away" with a nice array of tools and activities, this is a good choice for very young artists.

EAGLE EYE MYSTERIES IN LONDON

22 20 18 **20**

Ages: 8 & up $$

Creative Wonders Mac/DOS

Kids/Edugames-Social Studies

A shiny disc, a humming box, a glowing screen and quiet children—Ah, my dear Watson, it is indeed a wonderful CD-ROM. The mystery is solved! *Eagle Eye* is "surprisingly interesting, challenging and entertaining." Kids have to ponder mysteries with the assistance of two teenagers and their laptop computer (welcome to the '90s). This interface is "well designed" and easy-to-use, and provides a substantial amount of British history along the way.

EAGLE EYE MYSTERIES: THE ORIGINAL

19 16 21 **19**

Ages: 8 & up $$

Creative Wonders Mac/DOS

Kids/Edugames-Social Studies

Foster your child's "deductive reasoning" with this "*Carmen Sandiego* for a younger group." From "The Case of the Vanishing Violin," to "The Cryptic Cavern," users will be challenged to uncover clues and weigh the evidence to reveal the culprit. While this "Encyclopedia Brown-like" title is scant on multimedia, "moves … slowly," and has little specific educational focus, narration accompanying the text is useful for young readers. Parents like "playing this with their kids."

EARLY MATH

20 18 21 **18**

Ages: 3-6 $

Sierra On-Line, Inc.   Win/Mac
Kids/Edugames-Math

Loid, a talking space creature, guides kids through these six "well-designed" math activities, each with three graduated difficulty levels. Some games focus on counting, beginning addition and subtraction. Others emphasize shapes—with jigsaw puzzles, pattern-matching and filling potholes with squares and triangles. A parent screen allows control of features and displays kids' progress. Simple graphics and spare screen designs don't push the state of multimedia, but it's still very "popular" with kids.

EARTHQUAKE

14 13 15 **14**

$$

Sony ImageSoft   Win/Mac
Science/General

This title is, well, not very earth-shaking. Although it manages to bring its audience to the heart of an earthquake's powerful natural forces, it does not shake up the state-of-the-art in multimedia. The video footage is "choppy" and "grainy," and information on what to do in case of an earthquake is "good" but "too general." Overall, this title falls a little flat, suffering from "superficiality" and "not enough actual quake footage."

EARTHSIEGE

14 20 14 **18**

$$$

Sierra On-Line, Inc.   DOS
Games/Role-playing & Interactive Fiction

While its sequel, *Metaltech: Battledrome*, was purely rock 'em, sock 'em robots, this earlier, "more involving" package has you fighting not for money but for survival. Pick a robot, any robot—then select one of eight progressively harder individual missions. Perhaps you choose to defend your home base against the nasty Cybrid forces. It'll take lots of practice with the "hard-to-control" interface, but the arcade action, industrial sounds, and "great" graphics are worth it.

ECHO LAKE

23 23 22 **24**

$$$$

Delrina Corporation   Win
Family

Echo Lake, the "first" family history creator, is a cozy retreat where you record and remember your life. Its "warm and inviting," "elegant" interface makes histories fun, allowing personal photographs (if your CD drive can, like most, read photo-CD), video, clip art and even (with soundcard and microphone) voice narration. "Extremely well-conceived," its seamless use of multimedia will "knock your socks off." Great for grandparents, if they have the hardware.

ECSTATICA

18 19 14 **16**

Ages: 17 & up $$

Psygnosis, Ltd.
Games/Action

DOS

Opinions were strong, but mixed, about this impressive interactive adventure. An evil force has taken over a once-peaceful Northern European village, and you're right smack in the middle of it. Many like the "fluid animation" and colorful cartoon graphics, but this game is extremely "violent," with "truly gruesome scenes"—naked people impaled on spears, for example. That, and "horrendous" controls, tip the scale for some. However you weigh in, the box says over 17 only.

EMILY POST'S COMPLETE GUIDE TO WEDDINGS

- - - **15**

$$

HarperCollins Interactive
Family

Win

The Empress of Etiquette offers advice on all areas of wedding planning, right down to recommendations for music, floral arrangements, reception menus, and honeymoon spots. This program helps set a budget, create the invitation list, and organize seating charts. Since it's not polite to stare at the computer screen when working with others, the disc sometimes comes with a copy of *Emily Post's Complete Book of Wedding Etiquette*.

ENCARTA '95

22 22 22 **22**

$$$$

Microsoft Corporation
Reference/Encyclopedias

Win/Mac

"The closest thing yet to a true multimedia encyclopedia," *Encarta* is an extensively upgraded version of Funk and Wagnall's. "Easier to use" than the competition, you can search by topic and keyword. The Wizard feature does complicated word searches by asking questions about what you want. Fun InterActivities provide six self-guided presentations, on topics like astronomy and immigration. Even *Encarta's* articles could use more "substance" but is still an "excellent" resource with "awesome" multimedia.

ESPN BASEBALL TONIGHT

16 17 13 **15**

$$

Sony ImageSoft
Games/Sports Simulation

DOS

There are "no shortage of options" for the serious baseball fan—begin with batting practice or simulate an entire season. But while the "opening intro dazzles" with a heart-thumping score and there are "a few amusing parts," it settles into a mediocre ball game, with only one pitcher's perspective from behind home plate. For a game that can use up 54 megs of memory, it's not a homer. Take a swing at *Front Page Sports Baseball '94* instead.

ESPN INTERACTIVE GOLF: LOWER YOUR SCORE WITH TOM KITE—SHOT MAKING

- - - 17
$$

Intellimedia Sports, Inc.   Win/Mac
Sports Reference
See *ESPN Interactive Golf: Lower Your Score with Tom Kite—The Full Swing and Putting*

ESPN INTERACTIVE GOLF: LOWER YOUR SCORE WITH TOM KITE—THE FULL SWING AND PUTTING

- - - 17
$$

Intellimedia Sports, Inc.   Win/Mac
Sports Reference
The premise of both the 2-disc *ESPN Interactive Golf* titles is that getting up close and personal with golf's all-time money winner will somehow vastly improve a duffer's score. Psychologist Bob Rotella's insights on the mind games in this exquisite yet baffling sport meld nicely with Kite's personable approach. *The Full Swing and Putting* cover the basics: the right grip, stance, posture and swing. Once you master them, *Shot Making* covers the most difficult shots, such as lobs, downhill lies, buried bunker shots and pitching from the rough. Despite postage-stamp videos, there's good content and individual how-to coaching is a nice touch. So that's how to lose that slice…

ESPN LET'S PLAY TENNIS

- - - 14
Ages: 12 & up $

Intellimedia Sports, Inc.   Win/Mac
Sports Reference
Tracy Austin, Fred Stolle and Cliff Drysdale give advice with 30 videos demonstrating proper form for beginners and intermediates. These tennis greats cover the basics in an instructional, not an interactive, format and without a clear pedagogy, they seem to be "throwing tons of facts at you, making a confusing mishmash." Ultimately, most find the title "too thin," without the in-depth information that tennis fanatics crave.

ESSENTIAL FRANKENSTEIN

16 15 16 16
$$

Time-Warner Interactive Group   Win
Literature
The monster has come back to haunt again—only this time in an "academic treatment" on CD-ROM. The disc contains the texts of Mary Shelley's famous novel and Leonard Wolf's book *The Essential Frankenstein*, an "extensive" interview with Wolf and video clips and posters from the classic movies. A "childish" Monster Bash game is probably best ignored. "Monster lovers won't want to miss" this, though many say it fails to "bring the monster to life."

EVERYTHING YOU WANT TO KNOW ABOUT SPORTS ENCYCLOPEDIA

19 19 17 **19**
$

Creative Multimedia Corporation — Win
Sports Reference

"Fifty major sports are given the SI treatment" and an additional 17 more esoteric sports like spelunking are given more cursory treatment. The cryogenically frozen game-show host that gets thawed long enough to give you tough trivia questions is on the weird side, but the encyclopedia of sports information is straightforward and "clearly presented." With lots of "photos, video, factoids, and hard information," this is a "solid disc."

EVERYWHERE USA TRAVEL GUIDE

15 14 19 **15**
$$

Deep River Publishing — Win
Travel

You'll enjoy browsing through the national attractions covered in this two-volume title—although you may be "less than pleased" by the "amount of coverage." Starting with your own hometown, you'll find this title only includes stops on well-beaten tracks. Text, photos and video describe destinations, but neither maps nor routing information appears. This guide is okay for family vacation brainstorming, but you'll need more information before packing your bags.

EXPERT TRAVEL PLANNER

14 16 18 **14**
$

Expert Software — Win
Travel

Cheaper than the competition, this is the vacation advisor for budget travelers. With a "sizable database of cities" *Travel Planner* can "take you to and from just about anywhere" in the United State, giving "reasonably intelligent" routing information. It's "easy to use" and has videos and slide shows of various cities that "kids like," but it doesn't include as many sites of interest as other mapping programs do. This is "tourist-class trip planning, at an economy-class price."

EXPLORAPEDIA: THE WORLD OF NATURE

21 22 21 **21**
Ages: 6-10 $$

Microsoft Corporation — Win
Reference/Kids

Explorapedia is a nature reference for younger kids. There's a "wealth of information" here, "excellent for non-readers as well as readers." Its 4000 screens contain photos, songs, 44 animations, 38 videos and brief, child-narrated descriptions of hundreds of topics. Kids dive in with topic or word searches, or select one of 16 natural environments to explore. The cartoon frog guide, and numerous educational games encourage "some thinking" in kids.

EXPLORAPEDIA: THE WORLD OF PEOPLE

19 17 19 **19**

Ages: 6-10 $$

Microsoft Corporation Win

Reference/Kids

"Crammed with fun facts," this title is a wide-ranging, entertaining presentation of general interest topics from atoms to zoos. Information is "nicely cross-referenced" and categorized by environments, such as city, home, art studio, factory, and scientist's lab. Kids enjoy the nonlinear exploration, making their own connections among the topics. Videos, songs, games, animations and whiz-bang sound effects make this a nice rainy day adventure, "sure to excite" young minds.

EXPLORING THE SOLAR SYSTEM AND BEYOND

13 8 16 **13**

$$

National Geographic Society, Educational Media Win/Mac

Science/Astronomy

This title is best described as four electronic children's books on the sun, moon, solar system and space exploration. The photo illustrations are attractive, but the exclusion of motion multimedia and "very few sound effects" begs the question "why CD-ROM?" The read-along text which highlights itself in concert with the narration will appeal to young readers, but the lack of background information and "primitive" interactive elements dampen the overall educational value.

EXTREME SPORTS

18 19 16 **19**

$

Medio Multimedia Inc. Win

Sports Reference

"Excellent narration, smooth video," great photos and sounds are put to the test of showing you all about 'extreme' sports. Some feel this disc is too passive, like a spectator sport. But it's packed with information, from interviews with the pros to where you can participate. Browse or delve into the details of a specific sport. If you're an extreme sportsperson yourself, use the journal feature and enter digitized images and audio of yourself, if you dare.

EYEWITNESS ENCYCLOPEDIA OF SCIENCE

16 19 18 **17**

$$$

Dorling Kindersley Publishing, Inc. Win/Mac/DOS

Science/General

This "beautifully done" title is a veritable rolodex of science. Four main topics, math, physics, chemistry and life science, are presented in a "visually appealing and informative" way. But there "needs to be more." The brief articles and biographies don't allow for any in-depth research. Physics and Astronomy are highlights. While some feel it "makes science crackle with … excitement," it has "no real activities," to draw kids to the computer.

C M U **O**

FACE OF LIFE
14 16 20 14
$
Creative Multimedia Corporation   Win
Current Affairs
Peruse the highlights of current events, sports, movies, books and fads of 1936–1972 as reported through "a stellar collection of images" from Life magazine. Searching is "quick and easy" and the trivia game will challenge your knowledge of the era. Unfortunately, photo essays and advertisements are not zoomable, leaving almost all of the copy unreadable. This slick but superficial treatment is "more like a commercial for Life" than a meaningful exploration of recent history.

FALCON GOLD
20 13 14 18
$$$$
Spectrum Holobyte, Inc.   DOS
Games/Combat
It's been three years since *Falcon 3.0*, and "it's getting a little long in the tooth." Still, this is the "most realistic combat flight sim on the market" and is packaged with all its add-ons—*Operation: Fighting Tiger; MIG-29: Deadly Adversary*, and *Hornet: Naval Strike Fighter*—plus an hour video on combat basics. It's an "incredible bargain" to get months of flying time for one price. Plan on spending a chunk of that time on the installation.

FAMILY TREE MAKER DELUXE CD-ROM EDITION
23 16 23 22
$$$
Banner Blue Software   Win
Genealogy/Family History
This CD "takes the drudgery out of genealogy" by being a powerful organizer of family information, including photos (with a photo-CD compatible CD drive) and a getting-started reference with an index listing 100 million deceased people with pointers to additional data sources, many of which the publisher sells for an additional fee. "Extremely easy to use," this "invaluable tool" is excellent for people who wish to explore—and especially organize—their family history.

FATTY BEAR'S BIRTHDAY SURPRISE
– – – 15
Ages: 3-7 $$
Humongous Entertainment   Win/Mac
Kids/Edugames-General
Oh no! Kayla's teddy, Fatty Bear, has made a mess of the birthday surprise he was planning. Things are scattered everywhere, and Fatty needs help finding them. There's stuff to do along the way—play goofy songs, compose original tunes and, once everything's assembled, decorate the cake. Although some parents find it "too cutesy," at least scattering things differently each time gives this "pretty lame" title longer life. Best for younger end of age range.

FIFA INTERNATIONAL SOCCER

– – – 19
$$

EA Sports
DOS
Sports Reference
This title has been superseded by *FIFA Soccer '96*. For information about both titles, see the review there.

FIFA SOCCER '96

– – – 22
$$$

EA Sports
DOS
Games/Sports Simulation
The reigning champion of video soccer games snatches another trophy with its second PC-CD release. Unlimited camera angles and meticulously rendered player animations, both vast improvements over last year's version, add to the exciting play and stunning realism. Unlike the bang-bang scoring of last year's *FIFA International Soccer*, the '96 version demands strategy, patience and an overall knowledge of international play. Dolby Surround Sound music, chants and commentary round out the package.

FINE ARTIST

22 24 21 **21**
Ages: 8-14 $$

Microsoft Corporation
Win/Mac
Kids/Art & Writing
Move over Michelangelo! Start in a four-story art museum which has different features on each floor. There's lots in this "outstanding" drawing program—not just a basic painting studio, but such things as a comic book maker and drawing tutorial too. All told, it's a "very entertaining," "informative" disc, which will keep your kids busy for hours (and not just because it can be "very slow") creating cartoons, buttons and drawings.

FISHER-PRICE 1-2-3'S

– – – 10
Ages: 3-5 $$

Davidson & Associates, Inc.
Win
Kids/Edugames-Math
Fisher-Price "falls short" in this effort to keep up with the times by going digital. It has only a few, not terribly well-designed counting and sizing activities, a "sticky interface" and practically no animation. Other titles cover similar territory with more successful games, more eye appeal and more "room for growth." This is a title that "will likely be collecting dust" before you know it.

FISHER-PRICE ABC'S

18 19 19 17

Ages: 3-5 $$

Davidson & Associates, Inc. Win
Kids/Edugames-Spelling

Hidden coins activate a jukebox which gives little ones a choice of three alphabet games. Using "good interactive teaching" and "excellent graphics," the games let kids do such things as choose letters to make words or hear a short jingle based on the chosen letter. The games are perfect for that slice of time when kids are just beginning to understand letter sounds; but be warned: activities are limited, so there's not tremendous staying power.

FLASH TRAFFIC: CITY OF ANGELS

10 14 15 11

$

Time-Warner Interactive Group DOS
Games/Role-playing & Interactive Fiction

"Don't let the three CDs fool you, I saved the city of Los Angeles from nuclear holocaust in just under an hour and a quarter." This "easy-to-use," "high testosterone" interactive movie puts you in charge of an "intriguing" and "violent" FBI investigation. But "overacting" and "choppy video" make for a title that "needs work." And unfortunately, in this less-than-stellar title, the movie repeats if you choose wrong—leaving you wishing that L.A. blew up already.

FLIGHT SIMULATOR 5.1

23 22 21 22

$$$

Microsoft Corporation DOS
Games/Simulation

Previous versions set the standard for flight sims and *v. 5.1* is no exception. "Detailed" and "accurate" enough to be used as a flight trainer, it packs in 12 regional maps and over 200 runways throughout the world. Fly one of four planes over incredibly realistic scenery and slow down for breathtaking views of such structures as the Kremlin or the Statue of Liberty. For serious pilots only—there's not a machine gun in sight.

FLIGHT UNLIMITED

22 25 22 22

$$$

Virgin Interactive Entertainment DOS
Games/Simulation

"Breathtakingly realistic graphics," using computer-enhanced satellite imagery, make aerial acrobatics in one of five different planes an incredible experience. One pilot reported it's "as close to flying" as you get on a PC. This is a snap to pilot, especially since many of the hazards of other flight sims—such as equipment failure and bad weather—are strangely absent. But without a fast 486 or Pentium, don't even think of taking off.

FLY FISHING: GREAT RIVERS OF THE WEST

23 21 20 **22**
$$

IVI, Inc. Win/Mac
Sports Reference

If fly fishing is your passion, cast a quick line in the direction of *Great Rivers of the West*, a "beautiful" and detailed interactive tour of six rivers. From Big Timber to McConnell Landing, just click on the map to access "useful textual information" including detailed maps, casting tips, river lore and fishing strategies. Information on lodges, guides and local fly shops can also be printed. One user calls it "the best title I have ever seen."

FLYING COLORS

21 24 22 **21**
Ages: 8 & up $$

Davidson & Associates, Inc. Win/Mac
Kids/Art & Writing

Adults are "totally amazed" to find even they enjoy this kids "favorite drawing program." Start with a clean slate or an already rendered scene. Choose from 17 tools, over 1,000 pieces of clip-art, and a variety of fonts and typographical effects to complete the masterpiece. Good editing tools help to refine, touch-up or change image size. The remarkable "color cycling" animation creates "a lot of neat pictures" with a "shimmering effect" that is "outstanding." "Best electronic baby-sitter available."

FOOD & WINE'S WINE TASTING: AN INTERACTIVE EXPERIENCE

16 13 16 **16**
$$

Times Mirror Multimedia Win/Mac
Wine, Beer & Spirits

Although the movies are "low quality," expert Steve Olson provides an "informative" journey through the wine world. The focus here is on wine tasting. Olson provides copious notes on 48 diverse bottles and elaborate on-screen tasting forms for your use, but beginners beware— many terms (stemmy, mangoes, papayas, wet dog?) are unclear and undefined. Also, if you want to taste his 48 choices, "prepare for a hunt" as many are unobtainable.

FOUR SEASONS OF GOURMET FRENCH CUISINE

14 11 15 **14**
$

Arome Interactive Win/Mac
Cooking & Food

Part of a cooking series, this title is beautifully packaged. Based on recipes from Thuries, a French magazine, reviewers agree that the 100 "complex" dishes are "elegant," but still dislike the CD. Complaints include "washed out" food photos, "no nutritional information," sloppy recipes that list unused ingredients, and "small," "choppy" film clips. Graphically, recipes don't suit the computer screen, with unnecessary use of multiple screens forcing lots of scrolling.

71

FREAK SHOW

21 22 20 **21**
$$

Voyager Company   Win/Mac
Avant Garde
The music of the Residents is visually brought to life with stand-out graphics, modeling and texturing. Start by visiting the freaks at the circus. Things get more interesting when you discover how to go behind the scenes to explore their personal stories. Users "looked forward to learning something new" each play and say they "don't want to know everything"—the sense of discovery is "too much fun." A visually stunning multimedia classic that's hard to classify.

FREDDI FISH AND THE CASE OF THE MISSING KELP SEEDS

18 21 21 **20**
Ages: 4-9 $$

Humongous Entertainment   Win
Kids/Edugames-General
Search the ocean floor with Freddi Fish to find missing kelp seeds for Grandma Grouper's garden. Click Freddi around the ocean bottom looking for clues found in bottles along the way. Kids keep busy with 40 screens, each with a treasure-trove of hidden, artfully hand-drawn animations. A math game and an arcade-style game round things out. The "jazzy soundtrack" and "excellent graphics" are enhancements. Some say it's "slow," but the younger kids don't seem to notice.

FREDDY PHARKAS: FRONTIER PHARMACIST

- - - **14**
$$

Sierra On-Line, Inc.   Win/DOS
Games/Role-playing & Interactive Fiction
Freddy is a pharmacist with a conscience in a depressed frontier town in this "wacky comedy." Players control Freddy's investigation into the disappearance of people and businesses in the town, solving "puzzles that are as funny as the characters." It ain't easy: parts of the game will stump adults, and it ain't much to look at—animation is jerky, the art looks like Atari and commands are confusing. But for puzzling pardners, this game is fun.

FREE PHONE

15 - 18 **15**
$

See *Pro CD Free Phone*.

FRENCH NOW!

20 13 17 **18**
$$$$

Transparent Language   Win/Mac
Language/French
See *Transparent Language Now!* Series.

FROM ALICE TO OCEAN: ALONE ACROSS THE OUTBACK

21 19 18 **19**
$$$

Claris Corp.   Win/Mac

Photography

When National Geographic sent a photographer to cover a young woman's lonely trek across Australia, they didn't anticipate the inspiring, moving story that would unfold. Users called this coffee-table CD "spectacular" and "beautiful," but there were a few complaints about "low interactivity," and that once started, "it was hard to get out of" it. Still, those with an "interest in Australia," as well as connoisseurs of "stunning photography," will treasure this disc.

FRONT LINES

15 17 14 **17**
$$$

Impressions Software, Inc.   DOS

Games/Combat

Strategy wargames are a special breed. There's little action—players alternate, clicking on units representing soldiers or vehicles, resulting in movement or combat. "Typical of the genre," this one is "tough to understand," and "even more complicated to play." Big businessmen of the year 2044 plan to take over the world from the politicians and the trouble is they have the money, men and materials to do it. Begins with "the most beautiful multimedia intro ever."

FRONT PAGE SPORTS: BASEBALL '94

– – – 20
$$

Sierra On-Line, Inc.   DOS

Games/Sports Simulation

This stunner feels and looks "more like the real thing" than any computer baseball game on the market. Both ball and player movement are "dead on." Choose between action mode—using real major league players in 12 different stadiums—or manage-only mode for armchair managers. And when the season's over, a draft lets you choose your players for next year. Unfortunately, this is a real "memory hog" and requires a lightning fast computer. *Baseball '94* is slated to skip to '96 under Windows 95.

FRONT PAGE SPORTS: FOOTBALL PRO '95

– – – 20
$$$

Sierra On-Line, Inc.   DOS

Games/Sports Simulation

Front Page Sports succeeds at every level, with individual player controls for arcade players, and realistic statistical simulation for numbers fans. This fully-licensed game includes every NFL team and player, and over 10,000 stock plays. If you'd rather work the sideline camera than play football, put the game on autopilot and take over the director's seat. The expanded camera system lets you view the action from any spot on the field.

FRONT PAGE SPORTS: FOOTBALL PRO '96

– – –

$$$

Sierra On-Line, Inc. DOS

Games/Sports Simulation

Continuing its impressive three-year track record, the 1996 version uses motion capture technology to improve on its already solid animation. Fully licensed by the NFLPA and NFL, the game includes the new Jacksonville and Carolina teams, and 10,000 stock plays. Three-way play options include league commissioner, coach or all-star player. The game lets you view the action from any angle, and a streamlined interface promises to makes this powerful football system easier to use.

FULL THROTTLE

22 22 21 **22**

$$$

LucasArts Entertainment Co. Mac/DOS

Games/Role-playing & Interactive Fiction

There's nothing quite like starting a game in a dumpster. This "humorous" and "creative" adventure game, has you guiding a "tough-as-nails" biker in a quest to clear his gang of a murder rap. Users like this game with "attitude" and a "nice blend of action and thinking." The graphics, animation and music are all "high quality." Some experts wished that the game "was longer." Nevertheless, *Full Throttle* makes for hours of "high octane" entertainment.

FX FIGHTER

18 19 17 **17**

Ages: 13 & up $$

GTE Interactive Media DOS

Games/Combat

Mortal Kombat II and *Street Fighter* go galactic! Choose from eight planets and eight arenas and take on eight alien boxers to become king of the universe. This "addictive" disc is easier to control than some of the other fighting games, but the manual doesn't reveal all the available moves, so plan on experimenting. The lively techno-pop, "dance-inducing" soundtrack and swooping camera perspectives are "top-notch" on a Pentium; but on a 486 it's simply "average."

GADGET

19 22 20 **19**

$$$

Synergy Interactive Corporation Win/Mac

Games/Role-playing & Interactive Fiction

A surreal interactive movie that asks: "Why does Horselover want your suitcase and how will he use it to save Earth from the approaching comet?" This "cool" title, produced by Japanese artist Haruhiko Shono, features cutting-edge graphics that some find eerie. Budget-minded players may wince ("When I spend $50, I expect to play more than just five hours."), but this adventure "draws you in," and entertains up to the end. And the graphics "leave *Myst* in the fog!"

GAHAN WILSON'S THE ULTIMATE HAUNTED HOUSE

17 20 17 19

Ages: 8 & up $$

Microsoft Corporation   Win/Mac

Kids/General

It may not be the most educational, but this kid's title has "good gameplay" and is "full of surprises." Move through the 13 cartoon rooms in Gahan Wilson's "weird" cartoon haunted house, looking for 13 keys before the clock strikes …13. The animations can be "jerky," but the wide-ranging activities —including old monster film clips, a hangman game and a weird music composer—promise a fun time. Some ghouls, although cartoony, "may be too creepy" for "young children."

GAZILLIONAIRE

17 15 18 18

$

Spectrum Holobyte, Inc.   Win

Games/Simulation

Monopoly champs, get ready to go extraterrestrial! This "addictive" game with "offbeat" humor and "sophisticated" economics keeps you busy managing labor, creditors, insurance costs, even the effects of weather. An "excellent" tutorial teaches as you play, making learning painless. Up to six players compete against six computer opponents to be the first gazillionaire. It could use slicker visuals and more depth, such as more planets to trade, but what's here is fun.

GEORGE SHRINKS

20 18 14 15

Ages: 3-7 $

HarperCollins Interactive   Win/Mac

Kids/Stories

Based on the popular book by William Joyce, this is the story of a boy named George who dreams he shrinks and then actually does. Joyce's illustrations are a pleasure, and with good music this "fun story comes to life" on CD-ROM. But with few animations that young readers can activate, "interactivity is limited" and, with no side activities or games, this story CD has a limited shelf life. Buy the book instead.

GERMAN NOW!

19 14 18 19

$$$$

Transparent Language   Win/Mac

Language/German

See *Transparent Language Now!* Series.

GET READY FOR SCHOOL, CHARLIE BROWN!

– – –

Ages: 4-8 $$

Virgin Sound & Vision Win/Mac

Kids/Edugames-Reading

Spend a day with Charlie Brown and his gang and play seven games and activities, like filling in missing words in a story and participating in a spelling bee. Underlying the story and activities is a 1000 word dictionary that illustrates and pronounces each word. Promising an early word learning adventure wrapped with 1000 classic Peanuts cartoons, and animation too, this one sounds good.

GINGERBREAD MAN

16 18 16 **18**

$

Ion Productions Win/Mac

Avant Garde

The alternately "dark, brooding" and "catchy, percussive" music of the Residents is accompanied by ineffable visuals, created by renowned animator Jim Ludtke. "Icky but exciting" images randomly morph; characters, "rendered in a unique, sculptured style" spill tortured thoughts. For some this is an incomprehensible "turn-off," but fans enjoy the "haunting" and "beautiful" sounds, the "sardonic" lyrics, and peering into "the mental recesses" of the "seriously warped individuals" who created this.

GIZMOS & GADGETS!

21 18 22 **22**

See *Super Solvers Gizmos & Gadgets!*.

GLOBAL EXPLORER

19 11 12 **14**

$$

DeLorme Mapping Systems Win

Geography/Maps

This "detailed" atlas has 15 levels of magnification that promise a close-up look at all earthly terrain. But at the high levels, the maps become "illegible," with labels that crowd each other, making street maps "useless." An "awkward" airline route mapper only works when you bring up both origin and destination maps. It includes information on points of interest, but not as much as trip planning CDs. This won't replace a good print atlas.

GOLF

19 20 20 **20**

$$$

Microsoft Corporation Win

Games/Sports Simulation

Tired of getting up at four in the morning for green time? This Windows-based frolic-on-the-links provides the thrill of whacking the ball without ever having to pay the caddie or leave your PC, provided you get the hang of the controls. While there are still those annoying waits while the graphics iron themselves out after every shot, this newest version is on course for 486s and higher. Particularly "enjoyable" for golfers; "get this one for Dad." Or Mom.

GONE FISHIN'

$$

Amtex Software Corporation   DOS
Games/Sports Simulation

Cast your reel into the Bay of Quince, and experience the "pure delight" of this "surprisingly accurate" fishing simulator. You select the appropriate weather, lures and location, and then you wait, wait, wait for a bite. The "quality graphics" add to the "charm" of this title. It's "too low-key" for some, but still "a great catch" for beginning fishermen, expert anglers or anyone looking to find "the Zen of fishing on your PC."

GRAMMYS: 35 YEARS OF EXCELLENCE IN MUSIC

$$

Mindscape   Win/Mac
Music/Appreciation

Mindscape has reserved you a ticket to the Grammys, creating a 3-D animated theater environment replete with artist performances, interviews, biographies and a "rather inane" trivia game. The slick art design is memorable even though "background content is lacking." Musicologists love the extensive database on award-winners in their respective categories, but, after a quick tour, general users have little interest in returning.

GREAT ARTISTS

$$

Attica Cybernetics Ltd.   Win
Art Appreciation

Forget the other features: buy this for the zoom alone. This "excellent" function, painstakingly renders works of art down to the cracks, and is consistent with the quality throughout this "intriguing look at the lives and works" of 40 European masters. Learn about "styles and schools" and see "amazing video clips demonstrating art restoration." It's a bit "slow" and you might disagree with "some omissions," but from Van Gogh to Vermeer, it's bound to deepen your appreciation of art.

GREAT LITERATURE PLUS

$$

Bureau of Electronic Publishing   Win/Mac
Literature

The real value here, of course, is the words. Over 500 literary classics are completely compiled on CD, with narrations and images. Readers can read them on the screen, print, or save selections. Most of the multimedia elements are "incidental" and "easily dispensable," although users rave about a neat feature that makes books "totally searchable by word or phrase." So what if you miss leather bindings or turning the pages? Just think of the shelf space you'll save!

	C	M	U	O

GREAT RESTAURANTS, WINERIES & BREWERIES

14	14	12	**12**

$

Deep River Publishing   Win
Cooking & Food

Fourteen hundred great restaurants, wineries and breweries. So where's Chez Panisse in California, or Le Cirque in New York? Nonetheless, some find this list "useful," despite the "unnecessarily difficult" search system: for example, restaurants and breweries are listed in separate, unlinked sections. On the bright side, the specific listings can be "great" and, for restaurants, usually include photos, sample menus, phone, credit card and other basic information, and even occasional recipes.

GROLIER MULTIMEDIA ENCYCLOPEDIA

21	21	19	**20**

See *1995 Grolier Multimedia Encyclopedia.*

GUINNESS MULTIMEDIA DISC OF RECORDS

19	16	18	**18**

See *1995 Guinness Multimedia Disc of Records.*

GUS GOES TO CYBEROPOLIS

–	–	–	**10**

Ages: 3 & up $$
Creative Labs   Win/Mac
Kids/Edugames-General

Gus, a large, "goofy" dog, takes kids to nine learning activities. These introduce language skills, geography, social studies and science, and are "uneven in quality and design." An ongoing search for Cyberbuds, designed to keep kids moving through the different areas, is fun, but the facts recited by the Cyberbuds are not always accurate. With "poor animation" and lyrics that "don't win any fans," our canine friend could use some gussying up for future ventures.

GUS GOES TO CYBERTOWN

16	18	18	**16**

Ages: 3-7 $$
Creative Labs   Win/Mac
Kids/Edugames-General

In this "not-too-original" game, the budding computer user explores the five stores of Cybertown, seeking 15 hidden CyberBuds. There are a variety of activities and it's an "easy-to-use game"—click on a book in the toy store to learn about volcanoes; count the bubbles in the pet shop to learn basic addition, hear the "high-quality music." But still, many say these activities are "predictable," and once the Buds are found, the game becomes "boring."

HAIGHT-ASHBURY IN THE SIXTIES

16 19 13 **16**
$$

Compton's NewMedia — Win/Mac
Current Affairs

Tune In, Drop Out and Turn On. Tune In to an index; Drop Out of a basically "unplayable" game, and Turn On to the heart of this two-CD set, an "absorbing" two-hour slide show by Allen Cohen, editor of the period newspaper The Oracle. All 12 issues are here along with video clips and "terrific" street photos. You'll find "fascinating" interviews with the likes of William Burroughs, Allen Ginsburg and the Grateful Dead. It's a "poignant" period piece.

HALDEMAN DIARIES: INSIDE THE NIXON WHITE HOUSE

21 18 22 **20**
$

Sony ImageSoft — Win
Current Affairs

H.R. Haldeman left a treasure for historians, pundits and Nixon junkies by keeping a diary of his time in Nixon's cabinet. This CD "enhances the book" with "good" hyper-linking of text and Haldeman's "small, but effective" home movies. Users appreciate this "intriguing" behind-the-scenes glimpse of political posturings and intimate confessions. Scrapbooks, photos, and videos (Nixon dancing!) add life to the hours of "fascinating" material, but make no mistake, most of this "time is spent reading text."

HANNA-BARBERA CARTOON CARNIVAL

11 15 17 **12**
Ages: 6 & up $

Philips Media Electronic Publishing — Win/Mac
Kids/General

If you like the Jetsons, Flintstones or Scooby-Doo on TV, will your kids like them on your computer? Kids play any of six simple games, each with 10 levels of difficulty, to earn the 15 letters that spell out Cartoon Carnival. But answering Top Cat's cartoon trivia questions or helping Fred Flintstone catch flying balloons is "neither educational or entertaining," and interaction with the characters is "limited." Possibly amusing for the "nostalgic" parents, not the kids.

HARD DAY'S NIGHT

19 17 20 **17**
$

Voyager Company — Win/Mac
Movies

Join the Fab Four in their first movie. This disc contains the entire full-length film, plus commentary, an interview with director Richard Lester, two additional short films, and a photo gallery. The interface is "simple" and "unobtrusive," but the movie is shown on a "tiny" screen. While the title may play for the next generation ("it turned my nine-year-old daughter into a Beatles fan"), most agree it's better for the "real die-hard."

	C	M	U	O

HARD EVIDENCE: THE MARILYN MONROE FILES
– – – 14
$$

WordPerfect Corporation Win/Mac
History
Was Marilyn Monroe murdered or did she commit suicide? That's the question this disc poses, as you play the role of detective, D.A., coroner or investigative reporter for this enduring pop culture mystery. Sift through evidence as you try to uncover the mystery of the sex symbol's death. This title is packed with conspiracy, intrigue and "interesting" Marilyn trivia. The game, however, "gets repetitive after a while." Only for true Marilyn- and Kennedy-philes.

HARDBALL 4
19 21 19 19
$$

Accolade, Inc. DOS
Games/Sports Simulation
For the hot-dog-and-action crowd, *Hardball 4* stresses play and movement that is "quick and smooth," but "lacks extensive statistics." While the graphics "make the game seem incredibly real" (with SVGA required to see digitized video players) controlling the players is a chore, particularly because the scale is distorted. "The baseball is as big as a volleyball and it's still hard to maneuver your fielders to catch it."

HARDBALL 5
– – – 20
$$$

Accolade, Inc. DOS
Games/Sports Simulation
With a computer tradition dating back to the Commodore 64, this baseball series achieves big league status at every level, from beautifully-rendered ballparks to the new over-sized batter-pitcher animations. The graphics have always been life-like, but now they are life-sized, with batter and pitcher correctly proportioned in relationship to the other fielders. Even with surround sound and Al Michael's play-by-play commentary, there are no undue delays on a fast 486.

HARRY AND THE HAUNTED HOUSE
19 21 21 21
Ages: 3-8 $$

Living Books Win/Mac
Kids/Stories
Harry hits a baseball into a haunted house and the spooky stuff keeps coming. It's part of The Living Books story series, where objects do funny things when you click on them, and words are highlighted as they're read aloud to aid beginning readers. The "graphics, sound, interactivity" are "great" and the story is "interesting." Some kids "get bored" without more "activities," and find there isn't "enough meat to it"; but most say "give me more of these."

HEADCANDY

10 18 20 **12**

$

Ion Productions   Win/Mac
Avant Garde

Don the prism glasses shipped with this disc and groove on an audiovisual extravaganza in the leading-edge tradition of Brian Eno and Robert Fripp. The full-screen "laser shows" sync up with five different music selections totaling almost an hour of very "novel" entertainment. Many say this 1990s "lava lamp" conversation piece "leaves you wanting more options and more depth," but if you're into mellowing out in front of your computer this is one "cool" disc.

HEINEMANN CHILDREN'S MULTIMEDIA ENCYCLOPEDIA

14 13 14 **12**

Ages: 6-12 $$$$

Reed Interactive   Win/Mac
Reference/Kids

An "easy-to-use" encyclopedia, this contains the text and photos from the 11-volume printed set, plus narrations. The approximately 90 videos and animations "need improvement," and the well-written text offers only cursory treatment, so users come up empty on searches for many subjects. Here's the real deal: kids who can handle this title might just as well use the popular 'adult' encyclopedias, so why not go "straight" to *Compton's*, *Grolier's* or *Encarta*?

HELL: A CYBERPUNK THRILLER

16 18 14 **16**

Ages: 17 & up $$$

GameTek, Inc.   Mac/DOS
Games/Role-playing & Interactive Fiction

Expect a devil of a time hacking away at the 40-odd puzzles in this intriguing, "very clever," yet overly talky adventure. But unless you crack the mystery, you may never know why the Fascist Hand of God party has targeted you, a renegade FBI agent, for extinction. Lush graphics, "great music," and crisp audio, however, don't make up for the hellish dialogue and performances by stars Dennis Hopper, Grace Jones, Stephanie Seymour and Geoffrey Holder.

HELLO KITTY BIG FUN DELUXE

19 22 19 **18**

Ages: 3-8 $$

Big Top Productions   Win/Mac
Kids/Early Learning Skills

With "adorable," simple illustrations, *Kitty* has pre-school appeal and educational content to back it up. A clever piano game teaches kids to play some basic kids songs and make and record their own music. Kids develop basic reading skills with a fully narrated, interactive story-making activity which lets them change story endings by adding a choice of illustrated key words, and then play them back. Simple to use, this is a solid starter program for preschoolers.

	C	M	U	O

HER HERITAGE: A BIOGRAPHICAL ENCYCLOPEDIA OF FAMOUS AMERICAN WOMEN

C 19 M 16 U 18 O 18

$

Pilgrim New Media   Win/Mac
History

A "valuable" reference on female heroines, from Marian Anderson to Lucille Ball, *Her Heritage* uses text, slides, film clips and audio clips in biographies of about 1000 famous American women. The "beautiful interface" and "supremely navigable database" make using this title a pleasure. Users find "too few" video clips—about 60 total—but still call it a "rare treat." Especially recommended for "elementary and middle-school students."

HERETIC

C 18 M 21 U 19 O 20

$$

GT Interactive Software   DOS
Games/Combat

One in a growing number of *Doom* clones, this "absolutely fun" game is set in a medieval environment, using crossbows and staves instead of shotguns and bazookas. With the same basic principle as its predecessors —"kill everything in sight"— there are "lots of interesting villains to fight," as well as "spells and other neat things." Perfect for those who find themselves staring at a computer screen for hours, trying to finish the last level of *Doom*.

HEXEN: BEYOND HERETIC

$$

GT Interactive Software   DOS
Games/Combat

The trouble with great games like *Doom* and *Heretic* is they eventually end. Thank your lucky weapon they invented sequels. In this follow-up to *Heretic*, you'll battle, either alone or networked in cooperative or Deathmatch modes, against creatures with 12 weapons. Swinging doors, revolving bookcases, falling ceilings, earthquakes and crumbling bridges all add to the excitement.

HI-OCTANE

C 18 M 21 U 21 O 20

$$$

Electronic Arts   DOS
Games/Action

Man, if you've got a Pentium or even a really fast 486, you'll experience PC speed like never before as you blow up opponents while your Hov-Car screeches around one of six courses. But even fast Pentiums may cough and sputter in full-screen hi-res graphics mode. "Speed is the key" in this "exciting" game. Take your eyes off the road for a second—just to glance at your readouts—you're dead meat.

HIGH SEAS TRADER

14 13 13 **13**

$$$$

Impressions Software, Inc. DOS
Games/Simulation

Barter your various goods as you sail from port to port. *Trader* puts you in charge of a 19th century ship, making you responsible for everything from hiring sailors to buying necessary equipment. But with "ho-hum" graphics and missions that start to look "the same" after a while, players are disappointed. Users also note installation problems and a lack of volume controls. This is not the title to buy if you are looking for serious excitement.

HODJ 'N' PODJ

17 20 18 **18**

$$

Virgin Interactive Entertainment Win
Games/Puzzle & Logic

On-the-run gamers will appreciate this hodgepodge of 19 "enjoyable mini-games," most of which are awfully familiar, and can be started and played quickly. No need to devote two hours to these "diversions," no sirree. There's a pseudo boardgame that links all the elements together to earn points to save two princesses… if you've got the time. On the plus side, the voices here are remarkable, and winning requires "good gaming, logic and strategy skills."

HOME & BUSINESS PHONE '96

– – – **18**

$$$

See *Pro CD Home & Business Phone '96.*

HOME PHONE '96

– – – **19**

$$

See *Pro CD Home Phone '96.*

HOME REPAIR ENCYCLOPEDIA

18 19 20 **19**

$

Books That Work Win/Mac
House and Garden

This "straightforward" reference helps users cope with a wide variety of home ownership issues, from getting chewing gum out of the carpet to buying a post-hole digger. *Home Repair* has an "excellent" search function, and no-frills video and animation that provide "comprehensive" instruction. Useful tools help calculate measurements and costs, and while it may not be as portable as a book, the CD-ROM offers a depth and variety that's tough to find on the shelf.

HOMETIME WEEKEND HOME PROJECTS   20 21 19 **20**

$

IVI, Inc.   Win/Mac
House and Garden
With video clips drawn from the *Hometime* series on PBS,
this title offers advice on a variety of home improvement
projects, from building a deck to wallpapering a room.
Simple clicks move you from how-to clips to related topics,
tips, materials, calculation tools and shopping lists of manufacturers. Just like TV's *Home Improvement*? Not quite:
injury-preventing advice at the start help keep the week-
ender's projects from being anything like Tim "The Tool
Man" Taylor's.

HOUSE DIVIDED: 18 19 18 **19**
THE LINCOLN-DOUGLAS DEBATES

$$

Grafica Multimedia   Win/Mac
History
A House Divided is an "excellent" program featuring a
video reenactment of the 1858 debates that touched on
issues of race and government that clearly still divide
people today. Though not particularly flashy, it has an
"intuitive" interface that enhances the dramatization with
text, photos, narrative and songs to effectively put the pre-
Civil War era into context. A "satisfying" presentation that
treats a serious subject seriously, without being dull.

HOW ANIMALS MOVE   19 22 21 **19**

Ages: 11 & up $$

Discovery Home Entertainment   Win/Mac
Science/Animals
You'll marvel at the many and varied ways animals get
around! "From burrowing to gliding," this title explains
the mechanics behind the moves with "superior animation
and videos," "beautiful sound, interactive graphs, experiments, simulations," games and text. An intelligent search
mode allows you to tease out lots of information. Science
and math are well-integrated, making it "endlessly fascinating" for classroom study or for families actively interested in nature.

HOW MANY BUGS IN A BOX?   - - - **19**

Ages: 3-6 $

Simon & Schuster Interactive   Win/Mac
Kids/Early Learning Skills
Based on the simple, elegant book by David Carter, this
title includes a multimedia version of the book as well as
eight bug-counting activities. While it lacks the class of the
book, the clever activities for pre-schoolers compensate for
the loss. Parents may find the bug characters irritating,
with contrived accents and "cool dude" talk, but two- to
four-year-olds will appreciate the humor, good graphics,
silly music and fun activities.

HOW THINGS WORK IN BUSYTOWN

Ages: 3-6 $$

Viacom Interactive Media   Mac/DOS
Kids/Edugames-General

Even better than its predecessor, this "entertaining" town, with characters from Richard Scarry's popular books, keeps kids busy. "Easy" to get around, kids visit seven locales where they manipulate objects to do things like make toys and assemble truck parts. The activities teach concepts like sequencing—i.e., you grind the flour before you bake the bread. The visuals are so-so, the program bugs seem "unavoidable," but preschoolers "love the content and the sound."

HOW YOUR BODY WORKS

Ages: 12 & up $$$

Mindscape   Win/Mac
Kids/Science

You are given the run of an "entertaining" lab, "chock full of animation, text and videos." Exploring leads to information on such things as various disorders, their treatments and prevention advice. A good wellness video is included. The cadaver leads to the "most dazzling" area— 12 animated tours of the body systems. However, the content "lacks detail," and without hyperlinks between sections, it's "too disjointed to be a useful reference." Best for exploration.

I HAVE NO MOUTH, AND I MUST SCREAM

Cyberdreams   DOS
Games/Role-playing & Interactive Fiction

Much of the anticipation for this post-apocalyptic adventure is due to the fact that it's based on the most famous short story by famed sci-fi master Harlan Ellison, a force behind 'The Outer Limits.' Assume the role of any of five characters trapped in the bowels of a super computer. Emerging with your sanity intact depends on outwitting the computer and exorcising your character's personal demons. Not one for the kiddies.

I PHOTOGRAPH TO REMEMBER

$

Voyager Company   Win/Mac
Art Appreciation

With over 100 photographs and accompanying narration, photographer Pedro Meyer documents the decline and death of his parents, who after 55 years of marriage died nine weeks apart. The "unforgettable" images and "quiet, yet emotional" narration create a moving experience. Meyer's unflinching and "elegant" disc is a testimony to familial love, and a dignified treatment of the dying process. Even though a complete viewing takes only about 30 minutes, this is one you're likely to return to periodically.

I. M. MEEN

15 21 15 **17**

Ages: 9 & up $$

Simon & Schuster Interactive DOS

Kids/Edugames-Reading

This *"Doom* for kids" blends gaming and educational content without the gore of other combat games. *I. M. Meen* forces kids to navigate tunnels and corridors, solving various grammatical puzzles in order to finish levels. With a little help from a friendly Hobbit, kids battle large spiders and trolls. "Pretty good" game play and responsive, "easy to learn" controls make for an engaging experience. Some adults, however, wish for more educational content.

IDEAS THAT CHANGED THE WORLD

15 18 13 **15**
$

Cambrix Publishing Win/Mac

History

Here's an idea: take a best-selling book and turn it into a CD-ROM. Reviewers rave about the "gorgeous," "beautiful," "darkly mysterious" interface and screens, even as they admit it is "clumsy," "confused" and "awkward" to use. More a history of inventions than a chronicle of ideas, the "interesting" contents do "not go into a lot of depth," and be prepared to "dig" to find information. A pretty good try, but it won't change the world.

IF YOU GIVE A MOUSE A COOKIE

18 18 15 **16**

Ages: 3-7 $

HarperCollins Interactive Win/Mac

Kids/Stories

A charming story of how giving an inch to a mouse (or to a kid?) leads to taking a mile. Good graphics and sound are pleasant and faithful to the appealing and popular book of the same name. But with little interactivity and no adjunct activities, there simply isn't enough to do here. Worse, the long waiting period between screens is "frustrating," as are the "long delays in video clips." This title neither replaces nor much enhances the print version.

IMAGINATION EXPRESS

20 20 17 **19**

Ages: 3 & up $$

Edmark Corporation Win/Mac

Kids/Art & Writing

Even kids can get published! This "powerful" tool lets children visualize, verbalize and transform their fantasies into storybooks. They write their own plots, create their own pages and print out finished works. The push-button menu is a little "confusing" initially, but the disc is "feature-packed" and filled with "the best" clip-art and pre-fabricated backdrops around. Though it's a prefab story-from-parts approach, many find it good for developing creativity and storytelling skills.

IN THE COMPANY OF WHALES

17 15 18 **17**
$$

Discovery Home Entertainment Win/Mac
Science/Animals

If you love nature shows, this "comprehensive" title immerses you in the world of the whale. Based on a one-hour Discovery Channel documentary, there's 45 minutes of video, 200 photos and narration by Patrick Stewart (*Star Trek's* Captain Picard). Watch these leviathans breach from the water and absorb their haunting calls while scrolling pages of information. Not a die-hard whale enthusiast? Swim to the video store to rent the documentary.

INCREDIBLE MACHINE 2

20 20 20 **21**
$$

Sierra On-Line, Inc. Win
Games/Puzzle & Logic

This may look like it's for the kids, but it takes a heap of gray matter to solve these 150 wacky, "incredibly addictive" Rube Goldberg-like puzzles. "Start off simple," but watch out as things get complicated. Try stretching rubber bands over gears that fire cannons that shoot lasers off mirrors to activate your kitchen toaster. You can play head-to-head or make puzzles for others to try. The first puzzle is freeing memory, which likely requires a boot-disk.

INCREDIBLE TOON MACHINE

21 17 18 **20**
$$

Sierra On-Line, Inc. Win/DOS
Games/Puzzle & Logic

Haven't had your wackiness fix since the brain twisters in *The Incredible Machine*? Well, you're in luck! Here are 150 more mind-benders, some easy, some "really, really hard." Help cartoon characters Al E. Cat and his mouse nemesis, Sid, destroy each other with Rube Goldberg-type contraptions. The animated cartoon introductions to each puzzle "get REALLY annoying," but "incredible puzzles" make this a "great product"—probably "too difficult" for the under-12 crowd.

INDIAN IN THE CUPBOARD

– – –
$$$

Viacom Interactive Media Win/Mac
Kids/Stories

Producers worked with the Iroquois Nation to insure the authenticity of this spin-off from the children's film and popular novels. Youngsters play in two separate environments: a child's room where they discover The Magic Cupboard that brings toy figures to life, and a woodlands area where they can explore Iroquois life.

INDYCAR RACING 2.0

— — —

$$$

Papyrus Win/Mac/DOS
Games/Sports Simulation
With the same full throttle excitement of *NASCAR Racing*, this title adds improved digital sound effects, finely tuned handling, arcade view (drive from outside the car), and multi-player options, compatible with the developer's new on-line service. Collisions are even more realistic, with dents and pieces flying from the cars. Enhancing the experience is an additional 15 tracks, each representing the actual 1995 racing season, with cars, drivers, sponsors track side scenery and billboards.

INFOPEDIA

15 14 10 **11**

Ages: 11 & up $$$

Softkey International Win/Mac
Reference/Encyclopedias
With three Funk & Wagnalls references, four Merriam-Webster dictionary references and Hammond World Atlas maps, this sounds like a great encyclopedia. Unfortunately, instead of being user-friendly, it's "user-annoying," with "lightweight" information and unimpressive multimedia. While it does have the "best-looking" maps of the major CD encyclopedias, others are "easier to use" and "faster." Overall, it "needs a lot of improvement" to catch up with *Grolier's*, *Compton's* or *Encarta*.

INHERIT THE EARTH

— — — **18**

$

New World Computing, Inc. Mac/DOS
Games/Role-playing & Interactive Fiction
Well, we've finally done ourselves in; it's a post-human world and animals have become rulers of the earth. As a shrewd fox, you must track down a stolen orb that predicts when the rains will come. If you fail, your girlfriend becomes a pelt for the leader of the boar clan. The animation is "colorful," the plot "fascinating" and the gameplay "challenging." Fun for pre-teens and teens, but likely to be a little boring for adults.

INTRODUCTION TO CLASSICAL MUSIC

19 15 18 **19**

$$

Attica Cybernetics Ltd. Win
Music/Appreciation
This title is "an excellent refresher" for classical music basics, or "a good tool to expand the tastes" of beginners. Neophytes and seasoned listeners alike will find the breadth of music selections—200+ titles—impressive, and the composers' biographies, insightful. Keep the disc playing while using other applications and enjoy a "Little Night Music" for those after-hours computer sessions. You'll warm to the "performance" environment which recreates an "intimate salon" chamber music atmosphere. *This is included in the 5 ft. 10 Pak Collector's Edition.*

IRON ASSAULT

12 9 17 **12**

$$$

Virgin Sound & Vision
DOS
Games/Combat

Somebody declared this the year of the giant robot warriors and everyone's jumping on the bandwagon. These babies are a little (not a lot) easier to control than most, but the actual rough-'em-up sequences don't get the blood pumping due to "lousy graphics" and "poor sound"—everything looks clunky. Better alternative mech fighters will likely leave "*Iron Assault* warming the shelves."

ISAAC ASIMOV'S THE ULTIMATE ROBOT

16 17 17 **15**

Ages: 12 & up $$

Byron Preiss Multimedia Company, Inc.
Win/Mac
Kids/Science

Asimov's classic robot stories "are a better read on paper" than on CD-ROM. The disc does little to make the stories come alive. This title includes a "fun" game that lets you construct robots from various parts catalogs, but even this activity gets rusty quickly. "Ultimately, it doesn't have a lot of playability."

IT'S LEGAL DELUXE

– – – **19**

$$

Parsons (Intuit)
Win
Personal Development

There oughta be a law…and it's probably here! This practical CD outputs 54 home- and business-use legal documents. Simple, but important, documents like bills of sale and promissory notes, are particularly useful. A Legal Guide explains ramifications and document terms; the Law Dictionary and loan fee calculator are handy additions. *It's Legal* provides an "easy, inexpensive way" to "reduce legal fees," especially helpful to "small-business people."

ITALIAN NOW!

– – – **19**

$$$$

Transparent Language
Win/Mac
Language/Italian

See *Transparent Language Now!* Series.

JAZZ: A MULTIMEDIA HISTORY

16 10 12 **13**

$$$$

Compton's NewMedia
Mac/DOS
Music/Appreciation

Here's a novelty in the world of CD-ROM: the once ubiquitous but now rarely seen Hypercard software. "Even big fans" may feel "ho-hum" about the functional, but black-and-white interface. The disc includes 24 text chapters, 80 music selections with scores and MIDI music (quality varies greatly by soundcard) and 100 classic photos of jazz artists—but only six movies. A useful academic tool.

JEOPARDY!

— — — **17**

$$

Sony ImageSoft   Win/DOS
Games/Parlor

Alex Trebek on CD plays almost as well as on TV. Test your knowledge in this "realistic adaptation" of the popular television game show. The game is "great fun to play with friends" who gather 'round the keyboard to buzz in with answers to trivia questions. The game "could use more questions" to keep it fresh. *Jeopardy* can get "somewhat repetitive" and would be "more enjoyable if it played a little faster."

JETS!

17 14 18 **17**

$

Medio Multimedia Inc.   Win
Science/General

Very informative, with a "fantastic blend" of video clips, audio narration and decent graphics, *Jets!* "sends you on a fascinating tour" of the world of aviation. The disc includes descriptions and statistics of 144 military jets, 33 aviators, two technical books and additional aviation history. Though some laud this disc as "comprehensive," others think it only has enough for "an hour or two of browsing." Probably best for teenage plane enthusiasts.

JEWELS OF THE ORACLE

10 20 17 **19**

$$$

Discis Knowledge Research, Inc.   Win/Mac
Games/Puzzle & Logic

Beware…not for numb-brains! The logic puzzles in this "challenging, challenging" game can be "incredibly difficult," with few instructions to help. Set in the mental labyrinth of a long-lost civilization, the "great 3-D rendered graphics" and "scrolling full animation" add a lot to this "very good" title. The interaction is smooth and well-designed for easy access to commands and movement. A must for users who enjoy solving, not shooting their way out of a situation.

JFK ASSASSINATION: A VISUAL INVESTIGATION

21 21 19 **21**

$$

Medio Multimedia Inc.   Win/Mac
History

Think you can weave a better theory than Oliver Stone? Here's your chance to try. This interactive historical database blends video footage, audio interviews and informational tidbits to create a "very carefully made" analysis of one of the great mysteries of our age. The only drawbacks are the occasional lack of depth and the incessant commercials that play during installation. Even if you're not an "assassination buff," most of us have "some curiosity, and this fills it."

JOHNNY MNEMONIC
14 14 13 **13**

$$$

Sony ImageSoft Win/Mac/DOS

Games/Role-playing & Interactive Fiction

Take a great story, make a bad movie and a worse CD-ROM. Since the disc has "more to watch than to do," thankfully there's some artsy cinematography (the Keanu Reaves film was produced separately). But there's not much to do and make the wrong move and you're dead, doomed to retrace many steps. Some gamers couldn't run it, "even with the help of tech support."

JONATHAN POND'S PERSONAL FINANCIAL PLANNER
– – – **17**

$$

Vertigo Development Group, Inc. Win

Finance

Sure, financial planning information isn't terribly entertaining; but if you want to get a hold of your money situation with a detailed plan, this title "fits the bill." Combining financial information, worksheets and personalized strategies, it's organized into chapters on such topics as assessing your financial situation and profiting from investments. The program ends with a summary report of your goals, so you'll spend less time worrying about money and more time playing fun CD-ROMs.

JOURNEY TO THE PLANETS
14 11 14 **10**

$

Multicom Publishing, Inc. Win/Mac

Science/Astronomy

Aside from "a few moments of archive video" and "almost no sound," this title is a passive, cursory exploration of the solar system. With no narrative context, the planetary arcana are presented as "a big collection of trivia"... "accurate, but not very compelling." Though some report "stunning" visuals, especially the short simulated flights over seven planets, the search function and word definitions are uninspired. This one could have been better.

JOURNEYMAN PROJECT 2
20 22 20 **20**

See *Buried in Time: The Journeyman Project 2.*

JOURNEYMAN PROJECT TURBO!
20 22 16 **19**

$$

Sanctuary Woods Multimedia Corporation Win/Mac/DOS

Games/Role-playing & Interactive Fiction

The "awesome" and "photorealistic graphics" in this three-disc time-travel adventure are so life-like they make you feel "like you are really there." Control your character's every on-screen step and become a time cop, out to capture time-traveling villains. With lots of exploring and combat sequences, it's an exciting journey for younger gamers. But some fuddy-duddies complain about poor navigation and "horrible" sound. *This game is included in the 5 ft. 10 Pak-Collector's Edition.*

JOY OF SEX

Philips Media Electronic Publishing   Win/Mac
Relationships

The best selling sex manual of the '70s is a dullard of a disc in the '90s. The title is an "almost verbatim" replication of the book, including the uninspiring pencil drawings. Because the "arch, condescending" narration lectures on sensitive subjects in the most clinical way and the "videos are very scripted" and unnatural, users lose interest pretty quickly. The only hint at updating is a scant section on the AIDS epidemic and safer sex.

JULIA CHILD: HOME COOKING WITH MASTER CHEFS

Microsoft Corporation   Win
Cooking & Food

If you like learning about food, then peel the Salsify and break out the Pie Weights. With over 100 superb recipes, 16 great chefs and Julia Child, this elegant title "really uses multimedia." Recipes, while not easy, are well-written and linked to helpful sections on Ingredients, Cookware and Chef's Tips. Videos are numerous, but unfortunately are sometimes "unclear slideshows." Julia gives helpful background on dishes, and narrates a fascinating kitchen tour. This CD cooks!

JUMP RAVEN

Cyberflix, Inc.   Win
Games/Action

Strap yourself into a hovercraft and go shoot some bad guys! While the opening scenes, weapon selection and animated sequences of this game aren't bad, the action falls short. Although you have a number of different missions, zooming around a city grid and trying to shoot down all the enemies gets old pretty quickly. Despite high aspirations, this disc winds up being a regular shoot-'em-up game, with a very pretty cover.

JUMP START FIRST GRADE

Knowledge Adventure   Win
Kids/Edugames-General

Even better than its *Kindergarten* predecessor, the setting for this excellent collection of activities is a cartoon school. Imaginative games include the Vending Machine, using U.S. coins to teach kids about counting money, and Serving Up Fractions, a race against the clock to serve portions of food into the proper fraction of a lunchtray. Kids also hear stories, listen to music and draw with an included art program. A great combination of fun and education.

JUMP START KINDERGARTEN

23 21 22 22

Ages: 4-6 $$

Knowledge Adventure   Win/DOS

Kids/Edugames-General

Jump into the classroom and hop-click around the room to get into any of 13 activities. This "outstanding" pre-school title "teaches skills painlessly." Despite a few minor design flaws, a few weaker activities and some occasional installation problems, parents are won over by the amount of "challenging," "educational" and fun activities. One inspired feature uses a talking rabbit to encourage kids to try things not yet used. "One of the best" for pre-schoolers.

JUMP: THE DAVID BOWIE INTERACTIVE CD-ROM

9 17 10 12

$$

Ion Productions   Win/Mac

Music/Interactive Albums

David Bowie: innovative artist. David Bowie Interactive: "shallow" and "silly" software. Take a "clever" tour of Bowie's office, enjoy "elegant" graphics, see some new videos, and listen to David reveal nothing in a few quick interviews. Edit, in a "limited and difficult way," the video for "Jump They Say." Re-mixing the one song consists of "raising and lowering levels." Also, there's "multimedia junk" in the children's clickable animations mode. Even fans are disappointed.

JUNGLE BOOK

- - - 16

Ages: 5-8 $

Creative Wonders   DOS

Kids/Stories

Based on Rudyard Kipling's tale, Jungle Book is a "colorful" and "engaging" interactive romp through a classic. The story is read to children, with certain words highlighted for explanation, and there's interaction with "cute" characters: Jazz (a French-accented paintbrush), Winston (an eraser), Nick (a pencil) and Sally (a spray can). The commands are simple and large, the graphics are "pretty good," and the story moves at a reasonable speed.

JUST GRANDMA AND ME

22 23 23 22

Ages: 3-8 $$

Living Books   Win/Mac

Kids/Stories

Spend a day at the beach with a boy and his grandma, in this 12-screen version of Mercer Mayer's book. It's one of The Living Books series, where objects do funny things when you click on them, and words are highlighted as they're read aloud. The graphics and interactivity are "super," and while some debate the educational value, all agree it's "fun" and "captivating." "For the young at heart," as well as the very young. You can listen in Japanese or Spanish, a "neat" plus.

KID CAD

15 19 16 **15**

Ages: 7 & up $$

Davidson & Associates, Inc.   Win
Kids/General

Junior architects design with a rich variety of 3-D building elements. "Surprisingly versatile," *Kid CAD* has features to zoom, use two viewpoints, and rotate objects. Buildings can be colored, sized and even textured in a "seemingly endless" number of ways. When the work's done, print it, or even better, "enjoy" demolishing it with a computerized disaster. A great concept, but moving objects can be "like playing legos with mittens on." For patient builders only.

KID PHONICS

19 20 19 **20**

Ages: 4-7 $$

Davidson & Associates, Inc.   Win/Mac
Kids/Edugames-Reading

The Busters, friendly cartoon monsters, add levity to a solid group of word learning games. They sing fun rhyming tunes and lead players to a variety of games that involve matching letters to sounds, learning about long and short vowels, and word and sentence building. The Busters are "entertaining" and "amusing" and are frequently turned to for reprieve when young wordsmiths are game-weary. "Excellent" for kids who enjoy words and some silly fun.

KID VID GRID

16 17 11 **17**

Ages: 6 & up $$

Jasmine Multimedia Publishing, Inc.   Win
Kids/General

One of nine full-length Hanna-Barbera cartoons is broken into squares that are mixed up. In this game, you race against the clock to reassemble the pieces as quickly as possible. At harder levels, there are more pieces, or rotated pieces. And when the puzzle's done, you can watch the cartoon. "Innovative" and "challenging," this surprisingly fun game doesn't teach much, but should appeal to kids who enjoy jigsaw puzzles and cartoons.

KID WORKS 2

19 – 18 **17**

Ages: 4-10 $$

Davidson & Associates, Inc.   Win/Mac
Kids/Art & Writing

A "talking word processor" with "excellent" drawing and illustration tools for wannabe communication pros. Kids write and illustrate original stories, then hear their creations narrated back with accompanying graphics in slide show format. A large selection of rebus stamps (images representing words) are included. The help system is "incredibly complex" and the menus "are confusing" so it takes some learning. Watch for *Kid Works 3* due soon.

KIDPIX STUDIO

22 22 20 22

Ages: 3-12 $$

Broderbund Software, Inc.   Win/Mac

Kids/Art & Writing

A "tremendous" creativity program considered by many to be "the PC paint program to own." The latest version of *KidPix*, animation, music and sound effect features are added to the already large repertoire. Some are disappointed that the printed pictures are small, and quibbles include "very small" onscreen buttons, and some difficult-to-find features. Still, this winner provides unending "hours of fun" and gives kids a "great" vehicle for "creative exploration."

KIDRIFFS

16 15 15 16

Ages: 5-11 $$

IBM Multimedia Studio   Win

Kids/Music

Take Five ... aspects of music, that is. In this open-ended program, kids have five rooms to explore instruments, scales, rhythm, timbre and melody. The tutorials can be "very confusing," and since the sound is MIDI, instrument quality varies. On some soundcards, Cymbals sound like "a beep." Though a few call it just a "sophisticated noisemaker," most think *KidRiffs* painlessly teaches kids a lot. In any case, it's fun puttering around with the instruments and melodies.

KIDS ON SITE

15 16 20 16

Ages: 6-10 $

Digital Pictures Inc.   Mac/DOS

Kids/General

Kids love construction, so why not let them get behind the controls of four big machines? Despite "grainy" videos, and only three controls, kids enjoy being behind the wheel and revel in the slapstick humor: dumping dirt, running over construction workers, that sort of thing. Pretty silly stuff that annoys parents but amuses kids. Enthusiastic drivers don't seem to notice there's "little in the way of content or activities," after trying all four machines.

KING'S QUEST COLLECTOR'S EDITION

20 19 20 21

$$$$

Sierra On-Line, Inc.   Win

Games/Role Playing & Interactive Fiction

This two-disc set is a compilation of "really great games." The "excellent" *King's Quest* role-playing series involve guiding a character through a quest, solving various puzzles along the way by talking (typing) to people and finding and using appropriate objects. This set includes the originally floppy-based *King's Quests 1–6*, independent but related stories which share the "same" interface. These games are like "crackerjacks"—they're similar to each other, and "you want to finish them all."

KING'S QUEST VII: THE PRINCELESS BRIDE

18 20 19 **18**
$$$
Win

Sierra On-Line, Inc.

Games/Role Playing & Interactive Fiction

This graphic adventure has 60 speaking characters, a fully orchestrated soundtrack with 100 melodies, and "Disney-esque" illustrations. Although "too-easy" for experienced gamers—the game helps makes a lot of the decisions, and autosaves itself before you die, for example—novices like it ("my four-year-old daughter's all-time favorite.") So, while "cute" for younger kids, experienced King's Questers find this one's a lot different from the others, and not necessarily to their liking.

KITTENS TO CATS

18 18 13 **16**
$$
Win

Villa Crespo Software

Pets

Want a disc in the kitten category? This "perfect owners' manual" is really a mixed breed. You'll walk down every path of raising a healthy cat, viewing talking-head video, with a simulated VCR control panel interface complete with fast-forward and frame-by-frame buttons. But there's no animation and just a whisker of interactivity, although "crisp graphics" and helpful advice on feline behavior and well-being make the disc an appealing stray to bring in from the rain.

KLIK & PLAY

20 15 20 **20**
$$
Win

Maxis

Games/Arcade

Bored with simply playing other people's games? This title lets you modify and make your own games. It comes with a set of more than a dozen games, allowing the users to modify them, tear them apart, or just alter backgrounds. Although the simplistic shareware games are mediocre, users unanimously feel "it's a lot of fun," being able to create your own versions "without programming." Fun for kids—and those who are kids at heart.

KNIGHTS OF XENTAR

- - - **15**
$$$
DOS

Megatech Software

Games/Role-playing & Interactive Fiction

Because it is based on the popular Japanese series, *Dragon Knight*, the "super graphics" are in the Japanese comic-book style known as "anime," which tends to get a little, well, graphic. (A separate add-on disk can make it even more revealing.) If you're into "sophomoric humor"—particularly loincloth jokes—you've found the right game. The interface is a snap to use, but the story itself doesn't rise above mediocre.

LANDDESIGNER MULTI-MEDIA FOR GARDENS

$$$

Green Thumb Software   Win

House and Garden

Even the most design-challenged landscaper can devise a colorful, healthy garden. Click on your choice of flowers, shrubs and garden furniture, and drag them to the garden plot. Unfortunately, the photos show washed-out garden-variety flowers, shrubs, ground covers and trees, which make for a flat presentation. While the interface is "easy" and the instruction is accessible, the plant databases are somewhat "skimpy," and the program tends to run "slowly" on older machines.

LEARN TO SPEAK FRENCH, VERSION 4.0

– – – 20
$$$$

The Learning Company   Win/Mac

Language/French

For both *Learn to Speak French* and *Learn to Speak Spanish*, thirty chapters feature stories, dialogue and "inventive" exercises, while following a purposefully nondescript American businessman on his travels. After short cultural video clips, chapters start with vocabulary screens which contain the program's "most powerful feature"—a voice recorder. With this, you record yourself and then compare your pronunciation with that of a native speaker. Exercises include a fill-in-the-blank type vocabulary quiz and repeating dialogue from the story. Despite "mediocre graphics" and game exercises that are sometimes "too easy," these are good, "complete" language programs "for beginners."

LEARN TO SPEAK JAPANESE, VERSION 3.0

– – – 15
$$$$

The Learning Company   Win/Mac

Language/Japanese

This title does not live up to the quality of the other *Learn to Speak* titles. With animations rather than videos and "almost no color," the multimedia is "a bit crude." It's hard to learn to pronounce words so different from English by looking at an animated—rather than real—mouth pronounce the words. Still, it's "easy to use" and has "easy," fun games. It conveys the basics, providing a foundation "for further study."

LEARN TO SPEAK SPANISH, VERSION 5.0

– – – 20
$$$$

The Learning Company   Win/Mac

Language/Spanish

See *Learn to Speak French, Version 4.0*

LEGEND OF KYRANDIA, BOOK THREE: MALCOLM'S REVENGE

17 18 17 **17**
$
Virgin Interactive Entertainment   DOS
Games/Role-playing & Interactive Fiction

Malcolm, the malevolent jester, is free and trying to make it back to Kyrandia, but at the speed this runs, it'll take him a while. Gamers may see *Book Three* as more of the same ("can't duplicate the original classic"), but the puzzles are tougher and boast multiple solutions. While the 3-D graphics and digitized speech are first-rate, Kyrandia has the dubious distinction of being the first game with a "live" laugh track. Oy!

LEISURE SUIT LARRY'S GREATEST HITS … AND MISSES

– – – **12**
$$$
Sierra On-Line, Inc.   Win
Games/Role-playing & Interactive Fiction

Larry, the eternal Lounge Lizard, comes back to haunt users past. Some will be chagrined—there's really only one full-sized game here. The rest is excerpted games and puzzles from other *Larry* titles. You interact by moving around and typing at people, like in the *King's Quest* series, but here the subject is Larry's sex life. Other tidbits, such as Larry Pinball, are "very funny," but fleeting. Only dyed-in-the-polyester Larry fans or complete neophytes will get pleasure from this product.

LENNY'S MULTIMEDIA CIRCUS

– – – **18**
Ages: 5-11 $
Viacom Interactive Media   Win/Mac
Kids/Edugames-General

A humorous take on the seedy circus scene awaits you in this sequel to *Lenny's MusicToons*. Five lively circus areas teem with games and activities. Stimulating educational content highlights physics (balance, weight, force) and recognition of musical patterns, but the real focus is fun, with some artistic creativity on the side. Many games involve coordinated use of the mouse. The "graphics and animation is limited," but "it's chock full of activities" and entertainment.

LENNY'S MUSICTOONS

18 19 20 **18**
Ages: 7 & up $$
Viacom Interactive Media   Win/Mac
Kids/Music

Join Lenny, a hip, musical penguin, in his Manhattan penthouse, for five musical activities. The highlight is Lenny's Theatre, where kids produce concerts, choosing everything from the star and back-ups musicians to the rhythm and tempo. Despite reports of install bugs, it's "very entertaining" with "good sound and graphics." Kids "love it," though parents wish it were "more educational." Some knowledge of music is assumed. Targets 5- to 10-year olds.

LEONARDO THE INVENTOR   17 18 18 **16**
$

Softkey International   Win/Mac
History
Leonardo is "shallow" and "disappointing" to adults, but younger audiences often find it "very instructive." This abridged journey through the life of the original "Renaissance man" has a scant 19-page biography and shows only a few of his artistic masterpieces. Although it is "fun," "easy-to-use," and a "good idea" for a product, its depth and contents "fall short." A good buy for teens and pre-teens, but older scholars "didn't like it."

LET'S GO: BUDGET GUIDE TO EUROPE   19 14 14 **15**
$$

Compton's NewMedia   Win
Travel
Need a map? A fact? Some "very helpful" language tips before you take off on that European vacation? Then this comprehensive package is worth its weight in ducats. You'll find a simple and pleasant interface, maps and oodles of facts. Its namesake "budget traveler's bible" can't compete with the film clips, lengthy explanations, and pronunciations that are included, but—and this is a big "but"—"the traveler loses one of the nicest aspects" of the original series: "portability."

LET'S PLAY TENNIS   12 15 18 **12**

See *ESPN Let's Play Tennis.*

LINKS 386 CD   20 22 22 **21**
$$

Access Software, Inc.   DOS
Games/Sports Simulation
Virtually playing Banff Springs and Harbour Town is great fun but in virtual worlds no less than real ones, a hook is still a hook, the beach is still the beach. Enjoy the gallery cheers when the ball drops in the cup for a birdie. Just grip and rip—go with the clubs suggested—but don't get too cocky. The golf goddesses are eager to turn a par to double bogey. Ah, just like real golf!

LION KING ANIMATED STORYBOOK   17 19 19 **18**
Ages: 3-9 $$

Disney Interactive   Win/Mac
Kids/Stories
Kids who like the movie find this 20-screen storybook "enjoyable"—at first. They can read or be read the story, and the pages include plenty of fun animations that kids click and find. But it's not up to par with other animated storybooks, and the three games don't win raves either: The Pouncing Game is "hard to use" and the other two don't offer much depth. With "not enough to do," this disc gets "boring after frequent use."

LITTLE MONSTER AT SCHOOL

22 22 20 **20**

Ages: 3 & up $$

Living Books   Win/Mac
Kids/Stories

Part of the Living Books animated, interactive storybook series, this one is a "nice follow-up to *Just Grandma and Me*," being just a bit more advanced. Kids can easily relate to this story of Little Monster's day at school. In keeping with the series, words are highlighted, production is top-quality and there are plenty of clickable objects that reward with animations and sounds. Best toward the younger end of the recommended age range

LIVE ACTION FOOTBALL

13 16 15 **13**

$

Accolade, Inc.   Win
Games/Sports Simulation

You get to play one football game with no "no injuries, no substitutions.... and no grand strategy." Coach by selecting a play from a limited menu and then sitting back and watching it happen. Al Michaels' play-by-plays are right on, but the game moves at a "slow pace" due to "constant interruption" by Pat Haden's frequent commentaries. Designed with "more sizzle than substance," enjoy the live action video and don't look for too much depth of play.

LIVING BOOKS

– – –

See *Arthur's Birthday*, *Arthur's Teacher Trouble*, *Berenstain Bears Get in a Fight*, *Dr. Seuss's ABC*, *Harry and the Haunted House*, *Just Grandma and Me*, *Little Monster at School*, *New Kid on the Block*, *Ruff's Bone*, and *Tortoise and the Hare*

LODE RUNNER: THE LEGEND RETURNS

18 19 20 **19**

$$

Sierra On-Line, Inc.   Win/Mac
Games/Arcade

If the last time you were addicted to a lightning-fast puzzler was with *Tetris*, try this one. It may look like a cinch for Lode Runner to snatch all the goodies, but each of the 150 screens is more mind-wrenching than its predecessor. You see, one touch from the Mad Monks and it's curtains. Great bonus: there's an editor to design your own screens.

LORDS OF THE REALM

21 17 20 **20**

$$$$

Impressions Software, Inc.   DOS
Games/Role-playing & Interactive Fiction

Ever dreamt of ruling your own fiefdom? Now you can with this "fresh" strategy game. Set in medieval England, segmented into myriad diverse regions, you must effect "true strategy" to rule your turf. Levy taxes, recruit armies, attack other fiefdoms and defend against aggressors. The interface is "clear" and "easy to use," but the graphics are simplistic. You get the goods...but not the glitz.

LOST EDEN

19 21 19 20

$$$

Virgin Interactive Entertainment DOS
Games/Role-playing & Interactive Fiction

Youngsters won't be able to resist taking a bite out of this not-too-difficult puzzle adventure story of good vs. evil. Help young Prince Adam of Mo save the human and dinosaur populations from Morkus Rex's hordes of rampaging T-Rex's. The multimedia is simply stunning with its "breathtaking graphics" and rich sounds. With "more style than content," kids and beginning adventure gamers will still enjoy solving the memory-related brain-twisters.

LOST MIND OF DR. BRAIN

20 22 22 21

Ages: 12 & up $$

Sierra On-Line, Inc. Win/Mac
Kids/Edugames-Science

Dr. Brain's brain needs rebuilding in this "interesting" title. By solving 10 sets of brain twisters, ranging over diverse subjects like music, computers and biology, you can put his mind back together. This is an "excellent game to assist/supplement schoolwork," and a "great learning tool." This "great family game" engages teens and adults, requiring a variety of mental skills. *Dr. Brain* takes a while to go through, but it's one of those that, once you finish, there might not be a reason to return.

LOST TREASURES OF THE WORLD

19 17 13 19

$$

Follgard CD Visions, Inc. Win/Mac
History

Jewels and coins await you, lost in sunken ships and abandoned cities. This title's search tools and extensive catalog of riches help you pursue lost bullion in your own backyard, or seek out mother lodes in any region of the world. If hunting for El Dorado isn't your bag, sit back and read some of the "interesting" folklore and adventure tales. Despite "tiny" text and video, and an interface that can be "clumsy," nobody can resist the allure of lost treasure.

LOUIS CAT ORZE: THE MYSTERY OF THE QUEEN'S NECKLACE

20 15 18 19

Ages: 10 & up $$

IVI, Inc. Win/Mac
Games/Edugames-Social Studies

Lose yourself in the fictional intrigue of Versailles, 1697—the court of Louis XIV. Bribing, eavesdropping and poking around, you'll absorb lots of history as you search for a missing necklace. There's a library for background info, and the card game challenges your knowledge of the era. Though screen changes can be slow and there's little animation, sumptuous graphics make this *Louis* a feast for the eyes. "Best enjoyed by those with a historical interest."

LOVEJOY'S COLLEGE COUNSELOR

18 17 17 **18**
$$
Win

Intermedia Interactive Studios
Consumer Guides

Lovejoy's features an "extremely useful" interactive survey that helps applicants sift through 1600 colleges and universities to find the school of their choice. The search uses one or more of seven categories, including difficulty of admission and tuition cost, to narrow the field. The brief videos of 96 colleges offer "marginal value," but a listing of 2500 financial aid sources, with contact information, and another of the fastest growing careers, are helpful. College-bound folks use this program "over and over."

MACBETH

– – – **20**
$$
Mac

Voyager Company
Literature

Karaoke *Macbeth*? Well, why not? In fact, this title is superbly done, with "excellent" treatment of the text. Karaoke helps would-be actors practice parts or just read along. The pronunciation is very well-done, and the analysis and commentary, integrated with little pop-up notes, is simple and "informative." The disc also includes large, high-quality excerpts from movies by Roman Polanski, Orson Welles and Kurosawa.

MAD DOG II: THE LOST GOLD

19 14 14 **16**
$$
Mac/DOS

IBM Multimedia Studio
Games/Combat

If the varmints don't getcha in this Wild West shoot-'em-up, the "grainy video" and "installation" will. This game "screams for better resolution" *Mad Dog II* is "exactly the same" as the original Mad Dog McCree, except that "the graphics are not as jerky, and it has buried treasure." A gunslinger's life ain't easy; this one's especially "tough to learn" and might make you feel like you've "wasted your money."

MAGIC CARPET

19 21 17 **19**
$$$
DOS

Electronic Arts
Games/Action

Hold on to your turban...here's a superbly crafted, action-packed adventure game—a flying shoot-'em-up with state-of-the-art graphics. *Magic Carpet* shows how far 3-D modeling has come. "Absolutely incredible graphics!" exalts one user. Fly a magic carpet, wield magical spells, and battle the evil creatures. A "thoroughly entertaining" and "very impressive," fast, fun ride. You'll need "two hands" to play, and "vertigo sufferers—watch out."

MAGIC SCHOOL BUS EXPLORES THE HUMAN BODY

20 21 19 19
Ages: 6-10 $$$
Microsoft Corporation   Win
Kids/Edugames-Science

Based on the well-known books and cartoons, this disc starts in Ms. Frizzle's classroom with activities like reassembling a skeleton properly. Click on the bus and, in a "magnificent" 3-D animation, it shrinks and is accidentally swallowed by Arnold. In Arnold's innards the "consistently fun" anatomy lesson begins. Here kids explore by clicking around 12 body parts. Despite slow screen changes, this is a "graphically rich, educationally sound," and enjoyable journey.

MAGIC SCHOOL BUS EXPLORES THE SOLAR SYSTEM

19 22 20 20
Ages: 6-10 $$$
Microsoft Corporation   Win
Kids/Edugames-Science

Just like in the *Magic School Bus* books and cartoon series, the versatile bus never misses a scientific adventure. While whizzing through the galaxy on a school bus, children learn astronomy basics with this highly entertaining, effective educational tool. "My son learned the names of the planets before he was four because he loved this CD." This "excellent" program helps kids see stars—"much enjoyed" by all who jump on board for take-off.

MAMMALS: A MULTIMEDIA ENCYCLOPEDIA

16 16 18 16
Ages: 7 & up $$$
National Geographic Society, Educational Media   Mac/DOS
Science/Animals

National Geographic has packed this reference title with 700 full-color photographs, 28 videos, 140 vocalizations and 600 pages of text that describe each creature in "fascinating" detail. Quality, however, is just as important as quantity: The video clips are slow and have "no sound," the game is just a little too academic to hold kids' attention, and users want more activities. "A good starting point for research, but definitely not a definitive source."

MANHOLE CD-ROM MASTERPIECE EDITION

17 20 16 17
Ages: all $$
Cyan, Inc.   Mac
Kids/General

"Would you like a cup of tea?" the rabbit asks, and you are off—into the bizarre, psychedelic world of *The Manhole*. Filled with strange objects, places and animated characters, clicking objects can lead to interactive segments which sometimes transport you to another part of the program. This "*Myst* junior" is "pretty slow" and some get "bored quickly" since it's "not goal-oriented." For those inclined toward an offbeat exploration, it does "reward curiosity."

MAP 'N' GO

21 14 16 **18**

$$$
DeLorme Mapping Systems Win
Travel/Maps & Atlases

A "powerful" trip planner that generates printable route maps for trips in the continental US, Canada and Mexico. Using zip code, phone number or name to specify places, it calculates routes a few different ways, including quickest and shortest, giving points of interest and hotels en route. Despite an interface that's "not intuitive," and a need for "more control of routing choices," with *Map 'n' Go* you'll have "no excuse for getting lost on the road again!"

MAPEXPERT 2.0

– – – **18**

$$$$$
DeLorme Mapping Systems Win
Travel/Maps & Atlases

A comprehensive street guide to the entire United States. Enter a city and street and *MapExpert* brings up a local map in seconds. Zoom in to see details of local streets. Annotate and print maps to take with you when you travel. Although it doesn't include a navigation feature, it's useful for copying and pasting directions into other documents. This is a "fun" way to explore old stomping grounds.

MAPS 'N' FACTS

20 13 19 **18**

$$
Broderbund Software, Inc. Win/Mac
Geography/Maps

Containing the whole world from Aruba to Zaire, this program is "not as flashy" as *3D Atlas* but is "easy to use" and "packed with information." It has no videos or slide shows, just a "fine selection of highly readable maps" and a "wealth" of statistical information. If you're after a fancy multimedia package, you're likely to find this "drier than the Sahara," but if maps and facts is what you want, *Maps 'n' Facts* is what you'll get.

MARATHON

19 19 20 **19**

$$
Bungie Software Mac
Games/Action

More *Doom*-style carnage packaged in "beautifully-rendered" 3-D graphics. You're on a mission to save a future space colony from hostile aliens, but the plot line is less compelling than the weaponry and gore. Single-player mode is good, but choose multi-player for pulse-quickening combat on a network or via modem. Heavy hardware requirements make this pick best for PowerMac owners. This is the "best first-person VR game" and perhaps "the most spectacular Mac game in years."

C M U O

MARIO IS MISSING!

－ － － 11

Ages: 8-12 $$

Mindscape
Kids/Edugames-General

Win/Mac/DOS

Poor Luigi! His brother is missing, and players must search high and low to find him. This fairly old title is pretty "simple" and doesn't pack much of a multimedia "wallop." Guide Luigi through 25 different cities, talking to characters, collecting items, catching turtles-gone-bad, and picking up clues to Mario's location. But act fast! The evil Bowser will barbecue poor Mario if Luigi doesn't find him in time.

MARIO TEACHES TYPING

20 19 18 18

Ages: 5 & up $$

Interplay Productions
Kids/General

Mac/DOS

Mario's chattering head periodically appears during the "fun" lessons that turn typing practice into a video-like game. Kids move characters across the screen, avoiding obstacles by typing the letter, word or sentence that appears at the top of the screen. Mario's hand at the bottom of the screen highlights the correct finger. Within lessons, pacing is not adjustable, leaving some kids "frustrated," but most find *Mario* "useful." Sound and animations can be turned off for serious practice.

MARIO'S TIME MACHINE DELUXE

－ － － 15

Ages: 7 & up $$

Mindscape
Kids/Edugames-Social Studies

Win/Mac

Mario, of Nintendo fame, has been resurrected into a series of edugames. In this problem-solving history adventure, the evil Bowser has used a time machine to steal historical artifacts. By using clues given in dialogues with historical figures, kids help Mario fill in reports that will get the artifacts back. "Interface hassles" make it "difficult to use," but kids are "motivated" to learn some history and enjoy this game.

MARTIAL ARTS EXPLORER

－ － － 16

$$

Softkey International
Sports Reference

Win/Mac

Peek inside the art and philosophy of twelve of the most popular martial arts styles. The disc gives an overview of the basic techniques and spiritual aspects of each art, allowing you to compare and contrast elements of each form. Though it might not have enough depth for practicing martial artists, *Explorer* has an "intuitive" interface and an "entertaining" style that can help newcomers decide which of these ancient crafts to study.

MASK: THE ORIGIN

11 12 14 **11**

$

Cambrix Publishing   Win/Mac
Comics

Who's laughing now? Why, it's 'ol big head—*The Mask*—as he traipses through his often-sadistic adventures. This so-called cyber-comic production is really just six full-length comic books, stuffed on a CD-ROM and "read to you verbatim." The "acting is moronic," the sound effects "mediocre." While there is a minuscule amount of animation, the whole thing is just "two hours of entertainment," and cheaper in its original paperback form.

MASTER OF MAGIC

– – – **20**

$$$

MicroProse Software, Inc.   DOS
Games/Role-playing & Interactive Fiction

Some people go to school, others have jobs. The rest may have time to read this game's 150-page manual and learn the 213 spells. If you're one of those, check out this "well thought-out" game that's "one of the best mergings of strategy and role-playing." Choose your wizard, build a city, explore strange worlds and expand your empire. Despite graphics "from the dark ages," there's enough "tough challenges" and magic to keep "strategizers and… RPG fans rolling."

MASTERCOOK SILVER PLATTER COOKBOOK

– – – **14**

$

Softkey International   Win/Mac
Cooking & Food

This "not very sexy" CD from California Culinary Academy Cookbooks is stuffed with 600 "appealing recipes"—far more than most books. Features include recipe searching, recipe sizing and shopping lists. Nutritional analyses and substitution lists (i.e. yogurt for buttermilk) are nice touches. But this CD "just doesn't use the medium." Multimedia stops at some unappetizingly grainy photos and advanced recipes often refer to basic ones, but "inexcusably" aren't linked to them.

MATERIAL WORLD: A GLOBAL FAMILY PORTRAIT

18 17 19 **16**

$$

StarPress Multimedia   Win/Mac
Cultural Studies

If nothing else, this multimedia look at our world is truly unique. Photographer Peter Menzel and his crew hit the road for an intimate look at the day-to-day lives of 30 "statistically average" families worldwide, revealing a cultural contrast that is "mind-boggling." While the "outstanding" photos are lauded for their color and composition, the videos are dubbed "mediocre and rare." Charles Kuralt's "believable" narration provides cohesion to this eclectic array of material.

MATH BLASTER 1: IN SEARCH OF SPOT 23 20 21 **22**

Ages: 6-12 $$

Davidson & Associates, Inc. Win/Mac
Kids/Edugames-Math

"Finally math is fun and exciting." The animated space story wrapped around these math games puts young math wizards on a mission to accumulate correct answers. Kids can choose between addition, subtraction, estimation, multiplication, division, fractions, decimals or percentages. With good graphics and great practice of math facts, this product "fully engages" kids, especially goal-driven types. Best in the 6–9 age range.

MATH BLASTER 2: THE SECRET OF THE LOST CITY 19 19 18 **19**

Ages: 8-13 $$

Davidson & Associates, Inc. Win
Kids/Edugames-Math

Help Blasternaut and his crew complete four "exciting arcade-style" math games to stop Dr. Minus from destroying their home planet. Kids assemble pieces of simple equations, shoot "positron pods" at the correct numbers to fill in equations, and use "logical thinking" to design "funny" beings in "Creature Creator." The games can be "hard to start" and "awkward in use," but with six levels "rich in content and educational value," kids won't get bored quickly.

MATH BLASTER MYSTERY: THE GREAT BRAIN ROBBERY 19 22 19 **21**

Ages: 10 & up $$

Davidson & Associates, Inc. Win
Kids/Edugames-Math

Characters in a spooky mansion challenge kids with math problems as they search for the stolen brain of the world's greatest math competitor. Logic and word problems touch on subjects like sports and hobbies that kids can "relate to." Pre-algebra is "treated with finesse," and helpful tutorials break down the problems. This program is "hard to master," so kids struggling with math won't "pick this up just for fun," but math wizards will enjoy the "great game play."

MATH RABBIT 20 18 18 **18**

Ages: 4-7 $$

The Learning Company Win/Mac
Kids/Edugames-Math

A circus backdrop, with inviting graphics and sound, sets the stage for this down-to-earth group of drills. *Math Rabbit* gives step-by-step verbal instructions, making the audio fun, accessible and useful to young mathematicians. The activities focus on simple counting, addition, subtraction and set comparisons. It's a "very good program" that reinforces previously learned math skills. "A little slow" for some, it's still a solid title enjoyed by kids who like straightforward math drills.

MATH WORKSHOP

Ages: 6-12 $$

Broderbund Software, Inc.   Win/Mac

Kids/Edugames-Math

Puzzle-loving kids go for these creative activities emphasizing math thinking. The program includes estimation, spatial relationships, logic, fractions and math facts. Humor is "sprinkled throughout," frequently eliciting "spontaneous laughter." "The antics" of the pins in the bowling game are a common favorite. Excellent graphics, "enjoyable" activities and up-to-date math education concepts make this "one of the finest" kid discs. Useful videos help parents teach math on—or off—the computer.

MAUS

See *Complete Maus.*

MAVIS BEACON TEACHES TYPING FOR KIDS

Ages: 9 & up $$

Mindscape   Win

Kids/General

Mavis appears as an animated cartoon girl visiting her grandmother's house. Six rooms in the house contain games requiring kids to type the right sequence of letters to help Mavis do such things as clean up the bedroom. But the graphics are "bland" and the animated visual finger demonstration is "too small to see clearly," seriously limiting this scaled-down version of the adult *Mavis*. This title fails to honor her reputation as the Queen of Typing.

MAVIS BEACON TEACHES TYPING, VERSION 3.0

$$

Mindscape   Win

Typing

This "great," highly flexible program is a "very simple, thorough way to learn typing." It lets you adjust for age level, skill level and the pace at which Mavis takes you through the lessons. In the lessons, blue hands hover over an onscreen keyboard, ready to demonstrate the correct keystrokes, as Mavis tells you what to type. Four games lighten things up and a skills-analysis feature helps monitor progress.

MAYO CLINIC FAMILY HEALTH BOOK

$$

IVI, Inc.   Win/Mac

Medical Reference

Medical emergency? Better hope the PC's on. Clear graphics and well-written text make an easy-to-use home resource for common health queries. But the interface is unimaginative and "clunky," art design is dull and animations are "brief." The content in the disc, as in the 1400-page, 10-pound book, is first rate. Full bookshelves? Get the CD. Otherwise, this "not very fun to browse" title is "most helpful when looking up specific ailments."

MAYO CLINIC FAMILY PHARMACIST

22 16 19 **20**
$$
IVI, Inc. Win
Medical Reference

Family Pharmacist takes the "refreshing attitude" that we should participate in our own health care and sets about demystifying therapeutic drugs. Keep personal profiles on family members, and the program warns about possible negative drug interactions. You'll find descriptions of medical conditions and options, as well as advice on early detection and first aid. An electronic pharmacist interviews you to suggest treatments. Poor animations show "little movement," but this is still a "powerful tool for self-education."

MAYO CLINIC SPORTS HEALTH & FITNESS

16 14 18 **15**
$$
IVI, Inc. Win
Medical Reference

Like most get-in-shape resolutions, this title starts out great and then fizzles. The first section quizzes you about your health and then gives you "canned" suggestions for an exercise program. The 'Journal' lets you track the survey results and add notes to a diary. Multimedia motivation? Forget it— videos are good for "visual distraction," but the heart of the disc, called Reference, is no more than a 235-page hyper-linked exercise and health book.

MAYO CLINIC: THE TOTAL HEART

22 17 15 **17**
$
IVI, Inc. Win/Mac
Medical Reference

Total Heart, a "retread" of the excellent book of the same name, gives all text, "but not much more." Animations are brief and "very simple," there's little interactivity, and "there needs to be more illustrations." Given its focus on heart conditions and their treatments, this CD is best for at-risk individuals who will find it "helpful in explaining" procedures, but they would do just as well with the book.

MECH WARRIOR 2

– – – **20**
$$$
Activision DOS
Games/Combat

A big, impressive game with graphics and sound to match. But if anything will tax your PC's resources, this is it; a full 16MB of RAM is recommended. Customize one of 15 battle robots, and progress through the campaigns, blasting your way through strike, defense and reconnaissance missions. While it's disappointing that the multi-player version won't be out for a while, this is still a breathtaking update of the original classic *Mech Warrior* game.

MEET MEDIABAND

15 22 20 **17**

$$$

Canter Technology   Mac

Avant Garde

This title defies classification, but could be described as scathing-guitar-soloist-meets-computer-geek. Users interact with one of two pre-recorded music videos—'Undo Me' and 'House Jam'—by modifying the events in the video or by tweaking the music itself. Some see this as the future of interactive music with its "clever" visuals and "impressive" design, but the music itself can be "annoying." Ideal for those who pride themselves on their "nerd cool."

MEMPHIS MATH: TREASURE OF THE TOMBS

19 22 16 **19**

Ages: 8-14 $$$

WordPerfect Corporation   Win

Kids/Edugames-Math

This discontinued product will probably linger for a while, but look for price reductions. Solve math puzzlers about fractions, decimals and percents so you can peer amid three ancient Egyptian sites and collect artifacts. Kids love the "spooky" tombs and music makes "solving the fractions fun." But lots of independent work is required—things aren't self-explanatory, and ways to calculate answers aren't offered. It works best as a drill for those versed in the basic concepts.

MEN ARE FROM MARS, WOMEN ARE FROM VENUS

13 15 15 **15**

$$

HarperCollins Interactive   Win/Mac

Relationships

Based on the best-selling book of the same name, this title helps guide you through the male-female communication maze. You and your partner watch videos of couples as author and relationship counselor John Gray provides commentary. Gray's role-play techniques can help you identify your issues, but some users feel that the advice is good for little more than small-scale spats. However, the interface is "painless" and it's cheaper than a Reno divorce.

MENZOBERRANZAN

19 18 19 **19**

$$$

Strategic Simulations Corporation   DOS

Games/Role-playing & Interactive Fiction

"Dungeons and Dragons fans" will recognize the genre immediately. Select two previously created characters or roll your own, and then it's off to Menzoberranzan. There are 31 different monsters along the way and you can choose to either fight or talk your way out of battle. While the graphics and sounds are standard fare, the script, real-time combat, and the "difficulty of the quest" keeps "both your mind and your reflexes on their metaphorical toes."

MERRIAM-WEBSTER'S DICTIONARY FOR KIDS

19 17 20 18

Ages: 8-12 $$

Mindscape   Win

Reference/Kids

Based on Merriam-Webster's Dictionary, this "well-designed" interactive reference holds 20,000+ word definitions plus graphics. Entries can be located through a search function, an alphabetical index or by scrolling. It's "easy-to-use" and includes a set of "challenging" and "enjoyable" word games. Words are pronounced aloud, a useful feature for children stumped by pronunciation symbols. Definitions are text-only. It's short on eye appeal, but does its job and is "way more fun" than a dictionary.

MICHIGAN AND NOTRE DAME FOOTBALL

– – – 20

$$$

Stella Interactive   Win/Mac

Sports Reference

If college football is a religion, then Stella Interactive is certainly keeper of the testament. Produced in partnership with ABC Sports, the CollegeSports Series is a library of college football, with each CD including videoclips, photographs, statistics, profiles of players and coaches, and year-by-year records. When you add a trivia challenge, timeline and Keith Jackson leading the tour, you have college football nirvana. Multiple football titles are planned, with basketball to follow.

MICROSOFT TITLES

 – – –

See *Ancient Lands, Art Gallery, Bookshelf '95, Cinemania '95, Complete Baseball '95, Complete NBA Basketball, Composer Collection, Dangerous Creatures, Dinosaurs!, Dogs, Encarta '95, Explorapedia, Flight Simulator 5.1, Golf, Musical Instruments,* and *Wine Guide*

MIDISOFT MULTIMEDIA SONGBOOK

13 17 17 13

$$

MidiSoft Corp   Win

Music/Appreciation

If you like fiddling with the stereo controls, you'll love this collection of 190 mostly old songs and musical excerpts, many with brief, "entertaining" background text. The "interesting—and interactive" part occurs after choosing a song. As the score and lyrics scroll by, you can tweak the performance—soften the flutes, turn violins into harpsichords. But beware - this isn't the Symphony, and MIDI sound varies tremendously, and some say the songs sound "horrible."

MIDISOFT MUSIC MENTOR MAESTRO EDITION

14 13 15 **14**
$$
MidiSoft Corp — Win
Kids/Music

This duet of music history and theory is out-of-synch. The theory moves quickly—23 terse screens take the multimedia harmony lesson from chords to half-diminished sevenths. The history is spare: bios of 45 composers (five paragraphs on Beethoven); "entertaining" descriptions, with sound bites, of 44 instruments; a sparse timeline and glossary. Musicians "will not enjoy" it, while novices will "get in over their heads." Perhaps a "tuneful" combination of education and entertainment for the rest.

MILLIE'S MATH HOUSE

20 20 21 **20**
Ages: 3-6 $$
Edmark Corporation Win/Mac/DOS
Kids/Edugames-Math

An "excellent" highly acclaimed program that captures its pre-school audience with six creative activities. Amusing cartoon characters engage little ones in the basic math concepts: pattern recognition, counting and problem-solving. Build a Bug lets kids add features to a kind of multimedia Mr. Potatohead. The Explore and Discover option, invites experimentation with numbers by allowing multiple satisfactory answers. The adult guide to computer-free activities is a helpful bonus.

MIXED-UP MOTHER GOOSE

17 15 15 **18**
Ages: 3-8 $$
Sierra On-Line, Inc. Win
Kids/Edugames-General

There's trouble in Mother-Goose Land—Bo-peep's sheep are lost, the cat's fiddle is gone. Kids must find and bring back the 18 lost objects. Each success brings a golden egg, and a catchy animated rock 'n' roll version of the nursery rhyme. But unlike open-ended interactive stories, here only the correct action earns the animation. Some are frustrated by "limited instructions" and "long unstoppable sequences" but young ones find it lots of fun.

MONTY PYTHON'S COMPLETE WASTE OF TIME

23 22 22 **23**
$$$
7th Level Win/Mac
Humor

And now for something completely different...This title by the masters of devilish wit "lives up to all its promises and then some." In true Monty Python style, this disc is loaded with random tidbits, hilarious excerpts and flying chickens you can shoot. "It pushes all the right buttons in the areas of humor, surprises and originality." As is always the case with Monty Python, "wasting time has never been better."

MORGAN'S TRIVIA MACHINE
16 19 19 **17**

Ages: 7-14 $

Morgan Interactive   Win/Mac
Kids/Edugames-General

With more than 1000 geography and science questions, Morgan is a trivia game with "the look of a Saturday morning cartoon." The interface can be "quite slow," and some take issue with the accuracy of some answers. But with lots of questions, a "humorous" environment, three games, photos and videos, trivia fans should enjoy it. Especially recommended as a group activity when players go head-to-head.

MORTAL KOMBAT 2
17 19 20 **19**

Ages: 17 & up $$$

Acclaim   DOS
Games/Combat

No sense railing against the gore in this "too violent" sequel to the game that made pulling out hearts a national pastime. Players who buy *MK2* know what they want—violence, vivid backdrops and a pounding soundtrack. "Moms are gonna hate this; it's really bloody." The format is the same as *MK1*, just more characters and powers. There's no manual for the "heart trick," but that won't stop the "experienced player" who "won't need instructions."

MORTAL KOMBAT 3
- - -

Ages: 17 & up $$

GT Interactive Software   DOS
Games/Combat

You've kicked, punched, and jumped your way through the game, seen the movie, played the sequel, watched the stage show, and now—another sequel? How many more ways can there be to make mincemeat out your opponents? Apparently lots. Eight new characters join the original cast, with a bunch of secret moves, plus hidden Kombat Kodes that unlock even more secret moves. And it's all supported by network and modem play. How much more could a Mortal Kombatant want?

MOUNTAIN BIKING
17 18 18 **17**

$$

Media Mosaic   Win/Mac
Sports Reference

Here's everything you might ever need to know about mountain biking, from artful falling to environmentally correct skidding. Sound, careful advice will help any biker who loves the ride, although some information "seems intuitive." The "slick" title is packaged with "effective animation," excellent graphics around a "straightforward interface," and a soundtrack meant to appeal to hip, happening mountain biking types. Good for the "enthusiastic novice" and "a lot cheaper than lessons!"

MTV'S BEAVIS AND BUTT-HEAD IN VIRTUAL STUPIDITY

– – –
$$

Viacom Interactive Media   Mac/DOS
Humor

While the popularity of these two annoying misfits never fails to amaze some, this CD-ROM sequel is for just such fans. Complete with the voices of the TV series' creator, Mike Judge, this one asks players to assist B&B in an attempt to impress their hero, Todd, an overbearing bully. The game is interspersed with music videos that contain the duo's "critical" commentaries. Most likely for fans of the show only.

MTV'S CLUB DEAD

15 18 16 **16**
$

Viacom Interactive Media   DOS
Games/Role-playing & Interactive Fiction

Like MTV, the music's great, there's lots of flash, but not much to do in this "morass of hip, 'virtual' reality lingo." Why are guests dying at the Alexandria, a psychedelic virtual resort? If you care, you'll have four days to solve a mystery "geared for the Wired Magazine set." The acting is hokey, the video grainy, the interactivity and dialogue lame, and the volume just off the scale.

MULTIMEDIA BUSINESS 500, RELEASE 2

20 8 15 **18**
$$

Allegro New Media   Win
Reference/Anthology

A wealth of business information at your fingertips. This title is based on *Hoover's Handbook of American Business*— a "standard reference" for executives. About two pages of "brief profiles" are included on 500 major U.S. companies. This means you can get access to 10 years of financial summaries, executive Who's who with salaries, and a "historical narrative" about each business. Not quite the key to the bosses' bathroom, but it is an excellent research tool.

MULTIMEDIA CATS

16 20 19 **19**
$

Inroads Interactive   Win/Mac
Pets

Like its canine counterpart, this fun guide to cats is "packed with photos, videos and text." It's stellar feature is the interactive feline-human matchmaker. Enter preferences in categories, such as head shape and hair length, and it then generates a ranked list of appropriate breeds. With only 41 breeds of domestic cats, it's a bit "lightweight," but with "bonuses" like a section on 11 types of wildcats, it still adds up to a cat-lovers delight.

MULTIMEDIA DOGS 2.0

19 20 19 **20**

$

Inroads Interactive Win/Mac
Pets

This fun guide is "packed with photos, videos and text" on 130 breeds and set in a "snappy, intelligently designed" interface. Its "neatest" feature is Fetch, an interactive matchmaker. Enter preferences in categories, such as kid-friendliness and size, and get a ranked list of appropriate breeds. After Fetch, information on feeding and training "seem like afterthoughts," lacking the depth of a good book, but for choosing a pet, this tour of breeds is the "dog's meow."

MULTIMEDIA IQ TEST

15 11 12 **12**

$

Virtual Entertainment, Inc. Win/Mac
Personal Development

The creators, aiming to be fair, have attached an introduction explaining why IQ tests are faulty and misleading. This will leave users wondering why they even bothered to buy the title. Playing it won't make that cheated feeling go away. Take the single IQ test, and that's it, except for a measly three short videos by experts "at least one of which is really uninformative." This package has no replay value, making for a "pretty costly hour."

MULTIMEDIA TYPING INSTRUCTOR

19 19 18 **19**

$

Individual Software Incorporated Win
Typing

An effective combination of "valuable advice" and "excellent functionality," this title instructs by having the user type along to news clips and old magazine stories, preventing the boredom of the usual repetitive system. Videos provide instructions on finger placement. There are a few standard exercises that don't quite measure up to those of *Mavis Beacon,* but the "stunning photos" and "fun" interface make for an entertaining and useful tutorial.

MUSICAL INSTRUMENTS

23 21 22 **23**

$$

Microsoft Corporation Win/Mac
Music/Appreciation

Practically a "Harvard dictionary of musical instruments," this is a veritable cornucopia of sounds. An eclectic, valuable resource covering 200 musical instruments, this is a multimedia treat for music lovers. Users feel it has a "solid educational basis" and is a "great way to demonstrate musical instruments." From African tribal drums to Chinese chime bells, from baroque orchestras to 20th century rock bands, all are described in succinct prose and sound.

MUSICNET

22 20 21 **21**

$

MNI Interactive, Inc. Win/Mac
Consumer Guides

With rock, country, jazz and other genres to choose from, *MusicNet* lets you sample many new and classic albums before buying them. Compile your shopping list electronically and place your order via modem. Despite the fact that "multimedia is underwhelming" and that some feel the 20 to 30 second audio clips are a "tease," this is a great, easy-to-browse way to expand your musical horizons. You'll enjoy the "good sound" of this "incredible" shop-at-home disc.

MY FAVORITE MONSTER

18 19 20 **18**

Ages: 4-10 $

Simon & Schuster Interactive Win/Mac
Kids/Stories

Mooky, the friendly monster, is your kids' guide through his not-so-haunted house. There are tons of interactive hot spots, some of which pull up letter and number games, as well as a few songs. Adults find this title annoying, claiming it "lacks structure," but whadda they know? Kids "are nuts about it!" They enjoy the excellent staying power it offers, and they like that Mooky character. Best for young pre-reading kids.

MY FIRST ENCYCLOPEDIA

18 20 20 **19**

Ages: 3-6 $$

Knowledge Adventure Win
Reference/Kids

An "engaging" title with "beautiful graphics and animation" and videos of real kid helpers who explain concepts and "make users feel at home." It's an exploration of ten far-reaching subject areas, rather than a classic encyclopedia. The science "stands out" with "effective" lessons on animals, astronomy and geology. Adjunct activities are included and there's a parent index to words covered. The music is distracting, but that's what the 'off' button is for.

MY FIRST INCREDIBLE, AMAZING DICTIONARY

21 19 22 **21**

Ages: 4-7 $

Dorling Kindersley Publishing, Inc. Win/Mac/DOS
Reference/Kids

This beginner's dictionary teaches reading skills and enhances vocabulary—but your child doesn't have to know that. One parent "loved" the program because her kids "like playing games more than looking up words." *Amazing Dictionary* successfully combines both, in an easy-to-use interface; it "will read every entry—particularly appealing" to kids. A "very good first grade/beginning readers" program. But entries are limited, so readers will quickly grow beyond it.

MYST

22 23 21 **22**

$$$
Broderbund Software, Inc. Win/Mac
Games/Role-playing & Interactive Fiction

This immensely popular title is "thoroughly challenging and engrossing." It combines stunning graphics, a great musical score and a "compelling" plot, to make an "incredible program." Users start on a lonely forested island but travel far afield searching for clues to solve a sci-fi mystery. Parents are pleased to see *Myst* challenge children "to use their higher cognitive skills," but may want to send the kids to bed early to get some time alone with this gem.

MYTH OF THE TEN LOST TRIBES

18 19 15 **18**

See *Beyond the Sambatyon: The Myth of the Ten Lost Tribes.*

NASCAR RACING

21 22 19 **21**

$$$
Papyrus DOS
Games/Sports Simulation

Car fanatics go nuts over all the modifications they can make on their stock cars; but first they need to tune up this program since it's "a pain to install." Still, it's one of the best racing simulations around. The driving experience is amazingly life-like, thanks to the heavy, powerful feel of the controls. Play against live opponents via modem or direct connection. High resolution SVGA graphics display dramatic crashes in agonizing detail.

NBA LIVE '95

21 22 18 **21**

$$$
EA Sports DOS
Games/Sports Simulation

"Great speech, SVGA graphics and tremendous game play" combine to make this "the best basketball for the PC your money can buy." All the actual players of the NBA are here. Play an exhibition game or go right into the season or the playoffs. Every detail is perfect, down to the parquet floor of the Boston Garden. If you dislike basketball, don't back away—there's something for everyone here, hoopsters and hecklers alike.

NCAA FOOTBALL

– – –

$$
Mindscape Win
Games/Sports Simulation

Thanks to this title, college football will come alive on Windows 95 multimedia systems. This fully-licensed simulation has actual teams, uniforms, logos and fight songs. Arcade fans and sideline strategists will have myriad play options to choose from, including modem play, customized playbooks, highlights of games in progress, and on-line help from the computer coaching staff. Using 3-D graphics, the designers promise realistic animations.

NEW DICTIONARY OF THE LIVING WORLD

20 16 18 *20*
$$
Win/Mac

Media Design Interactive
Kids/Science

Comprised of an encyclopedia, mini-biographies on 180 biologists, a lesson on taxonomy, and the complete text of Darwin's *Origin of the Species*, this CD's greatest strength is its wealth of detail about the animal kingdom. There's not a lot of video, but what's here can be seen in a large screen option and you can do four-parameter searches that are lighting fast. Though the disc "lacks key components such as hyperlinks," it's a fun field trip for the armchair biologist—"the photographs positively glow."

NEW KID ON THE BLOCK

23 23 24 *22*
Ages: 6-10 $$
Win/Mac

Living Books
Kids/Stories & Poems

Poetry comes to life in this animated disc featuring 18 "witty" poems. It's part of The Living Books series, where objects do funny things when you click on them, and words are highlighted as they're read aloud to aid beginning readers. Jack Prelutsky's humor is irresistible to kids, and many adults, making this a "favorite" CD. The animations are good and there are plenty of objects to click "A great introduction to poetry" for youngsters.

NFL PRO LEAGUE FOOTBALL

- - - *20*
$$
IBM Multimedia Studio DOS
Games/Sports Simulation

This game promises a Sunday afternoon that never ends, with every pro team from 1961 to the present, including historically accurate uniforms. Every player on every team is rated, and with 200 offensive and defensive plays, the strategy options are endless. If the playbook is too small, design plays on the fly, including customized pass routes, motion and pulling guards. Modem play is exciting, and draft league fans can easily create teams and edit players.

NHL 96

- - - *23*
$$$
EA Sports DOS
Games/Sports Simulation

Now in its third generation, *NHL 96* becomes a true multimedia hockey simulation, with new 3-D player animations, video interviews with star players, modem play, expanded strategies and greatly improved artificial intelligence. Turn up your speakers and enjoy stadium-specific organ music and sound effects, while scanning a complete set of 342 high-resolution Donruss Hockey Cards. Pure heaven for hockey fans.

NHL HOCKEY 95

18 17 18 18
$$$
EA Sports   DOS
Games/Sports Simulation

Gamers may pass this off as "just another hockey game," but until NHL 96, it was the best available for the PC—sort of a back-handed compliment, since the game systems (Sega and Nintendo) seem to do hockey much better. Skate a game, go through the 84-game season or jump to the playoffs. Either compete against the PC, or find as many as 26 close friends to pummel.

NILE: PASSAGE TO EGYPT

21 21 19 21
Ages: 11 & up $$
Discovery Home Entertainment   Win/Mac
Cultural Studies

Climb aboard an ancient river boat for this interactive journey up the mighty Nile, where you can explore points of interest in ancient and modern Egypt. Independently, or with any of 18 available guided tours, you can investigate food, language, science, religion and other aspects of Egyptian culture. Users enjoyed the "excellent graphics" and "great" boat-simulation interface. With a wide variety of activities, this title "goes beyond reference" into the realm of entertainment.

NINE MONTH MIRACLE

19 20 20 19
$$
A.D.A.M. Software, Inc.   Win/Mac
Science/Anatomy

This "well-designed" disc includes some basic anatomy, but at its heart is the Family Album, a tour of the nine months of pregnancy. The content is designed for both adults and kids, though expectant parents, information sponges that they are, may find it "simplistic." *Miracle* has a "lighthearted" (some say "hokey") style, four interactive games and "vivid and awe-inspiring" images. The child's view of pregnancy should help ease parents through the "difficult task" of explaining things to preteens.

NOCTROPOLIS

17 19 18 18
$$
Electronic Arts   DOS
Games/Role-playing & Interactive Fiction

This "innovative" comic lover's dream is a "hilarious" heroic adventure. Play the role of depressed artist Peter Grey, sucked into his own comic book. To defeat the Noctropolis bad-guys and go home, he must complete the right tasks by exploring his own creation. Full-motion video and "beautiful" graphics "help the title stay exciting," and a "unique" "friendly" interface makes it easy-to-use. While "inexperienced gamers might be stumped," others find it's "a little too easy."

OCEAN PLANET

Ages: 7 & up $$

Discovery Home Entertainment Win/Mac

Science/General

Navigate easily through an Oceanarium environment that explores the oceans and man's impact upon them. Content is presented in a slide show format, and answers questions such as 'What causes currents?' An undersea theater plays a 14-minute video in the tradition of the Discovery Channel. You can query a panel of experts on ten hot ocean topics. Overall, the depth of content is disappointing and, without any elements of fun, unappealing to young users.

OCEANLIFE, VOLUME 4: THE GREAT BARRIER REEF

17 19 18 18

$$

Sumeria Inc. Win/Mac

Science/General

Fish lovers enjoy this two-disc title, but for others it's "a lot of fish but not a lot of depth." While the disc has "nice pictures," the undersea movie scenes can be murky, not ideal for educational purposes. Also, the maps are sparse, with no video or narration. Where does it excel? With 250 species of fish, three hours of video and a nice soundtrack, serious underwater buffs might take the plunge.

ONE TRIBE

19 18 14 18

$$

Virgin Sound & Vision Win/Mac

Cultural Studies

Explore world cultures through videos, photos, maps and music with this "very informative" disc. Its unconventional interface is at times cryptic so navigating "can be confusing", but the journey—not the destination—is what the disc is about. You'll be charmed by the hundreds of "captivating" photos showing the customs, architecture and landscape of more than 200 countries. This is a great way to "meet the peoples of the world" without leaving your chair.

OREGON TRAIL II

23 22 20 22

Ages: 10-16 $$$

MECC Win/Mac

Kids/Edugames-Social Studies

Become a westward emigrant in the mid-1800s trying to survive the journey. This updated version of *Oregon Trail* includes 3-D graphics, a printable trip diary, video and sound effects to make it like you're "really on the trail." Period western music that's "a pleasure" varies from "sentimental to toe-tapping," enhancing this "fun historical trip" that "really saves on gas." So stock the wagon and get on the trail with this "educational and engrossing" game.

OUTNUMBERED!

15 15 15 **15**

See *Super Solvers Outnumbered!*.

OUTPOST

20 15 17 **19**

$$$

Sierra On-Line, Inc.
Games/Simulation

Win/Mac/DOS

Picture "sim-city in outer space." In this "elaborate" and difficult simulation, the earth's been wiped out and you and your colonists must find a planet to inhabit. It's a great idea, with lots of scientific "accuracy." Unfortunately, early versions were loaded with bugs and the "package description," describing unbuilt features, just "doesn't equal the product." If it works, a strong product; when it doesn't, stay on earth.

PANIC IN THE PARK

– – – **15**

$$$

WarnerActive
Games/Mystery

Win/Mac

Choppy video sets the stage for this interactive adventure on three discs. As the story unfolds, you are a reporter helping the Good Twin save Sky View Amusement Park from her Evil Twin sister. Wander the park, collecting clues in order to find the lost land deed. Along the way, score points and get the tokens you need by playing classic carnival games. Before getting far you'll need to read the short manual. The reward is hours of fun and adventure.

PANZER GENERAL

20 21 20 **20**

$$$

Strategic Simulations Corporation
Games/Combat

DOS

If goose-stepping through Europe is your thing, this is "one of the very best wargames" on the market, "easy enough for newcomers" but realistic enough for hard-core fans. This turn-based military simulation serves up 36 separate missions with a choice of three levels of difficulty. If you are successful, you get to keep marching…all the way to Washington. The additional use of "video clips and speech" make this first-rate.

PAPARAZZI! TALES OF TINSELTOWN

19 18 12 **17**

$

Activision
Games/Role-playing & Interactive Fiction

Win/Mac

A good adventure game that will suck you in and drive you crazy. That's *Paparazzi*, and it doesn't get easier once you master the difficult interface. More than just an "original idea," it's also "a side-splitting" title. You'll harass "hilarious parodies" of real celebs, and when you get a photo, sell it to a really sleazy mag, just like the pros. If you want a game with great video, an impossible puzzle and a "ton of entertainment," shoot here.

PARENTS' GUIDE TO MONEY

$$
Intuit Win
Finance

Did you know that the average expense of a baby in its first year is $8000? If you didn't, and you're planning on children, take a peek at this interactive program which covers child care, health care, college planning and much more. Worksheets allow you to budget and make projections based on your particular circumstances. The interface is pleasant to use, and the presentation well-sprinkled with videos of real people and experts providing helpful advice.

PASSAGE TO VIETNAM

23 21 23 **23**

$$
Against All Odds Productions Win/Mac
Cultural Studies

Take a beautifully narrated trip through a Vietnam known by few. This "gorgeous, breathtaking" disc sensitively examines the lives, loves and losses of the Vietnamese people. Weddings are juxtaposed with funerals, and the "shattered" country's "natural beauty still shines through." The interface is unique—a rotating cube, which saves space and confusion. A 3-D video narrator and thoughtful, well-written text guide you through many of the exhibits. "A stunning achievement."

PASSION FOR ART

21 22 21 **21**

$$
Corbis Publishing Win/Mac
Art Appreciation

A breathtaking collection of Impressionist paintings, hidden for seventy years by an eccentric, very rich collector. Well, the legendary museum of Dr. Barnes is now open for your multimedia pleasure, and what a "delight" it is. Tour the museum with guides or on your own, encountering the visions of artists such as Renoir, Van Gogh, Degas and Matisse along the way. A "fascinating way to observe and learn" for the casual patron, unadulterated joy for art enthusiasts.

PEOPLE: 20 YEARS OF POP CULTURE

17 16 16 **16**

$
Voyager Company Win/Mac
Current Affairs

Twenty years of Elvis—alive and dead. Thirty-two covers with Princess Diana. Plus all the hunks, babes and dysfunctional families who've sashayed through the pages of this star-gazer's bible. This title features *People* covers dating back to 1974, selected stories and other multimedia goodies. That's a lotta doctor's office visits. Some searches come up wanting—does anyone seeking feminism want to gaze at *Charlie's Angels*? Sure, it's "fluff," but it's "interesting" fluff.

PERFECT GENERAL II

19 19 18 **19**

$$

American Laser Games DOS

Games/Combat

The war simulation for people who hate war sims—most of the "details are so intuitive," you won't need the traditional encyclopedia-sized manual. This upgrade from *PG1* features more colorful graphics, new scenarios, a tougher PC opponent, and "more bells and whistles." While playing against the PC is a blast, head-to-head combat can't be beat, whether it's at the same computer, over a modem or—get this—over the Internet.

PERFECT RESUME

16 12 13 **16**

$$

Davidson & Associates, Inc. Win

Personal Development

Okay, maybe it's not quite perfect, but this title can help you put together a good CV. Customizable templates help ease the pain of resume-writing, while career counselor Tom Jackson offers "friendly advice" on how to effectively emphasize your strong points, along with video clips and "excellent tips" on career focus, interviews, and follow-up. It may not be "particularly fun" or exceptionally fancy, but it just might be your ticket to that corner office.

PETER AND THE WOLF

19 18 18 **18**

See *Chuck Jones' Peter and the Wolf*.

PETER PAN

22 22 22 **21**

Ages: 6-10 $$

Creative Wonders Mac/DOS

Kids/Stories

Help Peter Pan save his friends from the fiendish Captain Hook. Loosely based on the *Peter Pan* story, this title gives kids problems to solve and fun tools to solve them with. Kids "love" controlling the sequence of events and interacting with the characters. The "very appealing" theme is presented with humor. More for fun than educational, it does "reinforce" reading skills. Installation can sometimes be a challenge, but it's "terrifically replayable."

PGA TOUR GOLF '96

- - - **20**

$$$

EA Sports DOS

Games/Sports Simulation

Real sports fans like to play with real pros, and *PGA Tour '96* delivers the big hitters, from Fuzzy Zoeller to Tom Kite. The '96 version is much faster than its predecessor, with new digitized graphics, a slick targeting system, fly-by views of every hole and multiple views of a golfer on a single shot. Serious digital golfers will love the new Instaview, enabling the user to quickly visit any spot on the active hole.

PGA TOUR GOLF 486

$$$

EA Sports
DOS

Games/Sports Simulation

"Computer golf simulations are virtually all the same," complained one gamer, although he conceded "this is a good one for golf fanatics." No doubt about it—the graphics and sounds are top flight, and the swings a challenge to control. Unlike competitive packages, PC golfers get to use computer-controlled opponents as well as nine animated PGA pros for playing partners. Unfortunately, like other golf simulations, it runs awfully slowly except on the fastest PCs.

PHANTASMAGORIA

— — — 20

$$$$

Sierra On-Line, Inc.
Win/Mac/DOS

Games/Role-playing & Interactive Fiction

This seven-disc game promises a hellish ride—and delivers! Guide your heroine around her haunted estate, and prevent her from getting hacked to pieces by her possessed hubby. Players pick up clues, solve puzzles and explore. "Fantastic," "realistic" graphics and "great" animation make this fun to watch. Player actions are "more advanced" than many games, but still, of course, somewhat "limited" compared to real life. Banned in some stores, its 'R' rating is not undeserved.

PHONE DISC BASIC INFORMATION

— — —

Digital Directory Assistance, Inc.

Phone Directories

Each of the three major Phone CD companies gets listings differently, and all claim, with impressive independent studies, to be best. Digital Directory Assistance uses specialized programs to scan the contents of nearly 6000 American phone directories. Their database has nearly 100 million business and residential listings, updated quarterly, which include Names, Street Address, City, Zip+4, State, 2500 Business Classifications (actually, SIC codes) and, of course, phone numbers. DDA's data has surprisingly few obvious errors, but expect some mistakes. Unlisted numbers are excluded and, since 20% of phone listings change each year, prepare to "update frequently" for the latest information.

PHONEDISC '95 BUSINESS

— — — 18

$$$

Digital Directory Assistance, Inc.
Win/Mac/DOS

Phone Directories

This single-CD business directory contains about 10 million listings. The data and search features are comparable to the company's more expensive phone books, but the listings are strictly business. For more information, see *Phone Disc Basic Information*.

PHONEDISC '95 BUSINESS LITE

– – – 17
$$

Digital Directory Assistance, Inc. Win/Mac/DOS
Phone Directories
This single CD business directory contains the same listings as *PhoneDisc '95 Business*, but requires searches to start with a business name or business category. After the initial listings are pulled up, searches can be further restricted by street, city, state, zip or area code. Now what was the name of that Florist on Main Street? For more information, see *Phone Disc Basic Information*.

PHONEDISC '95 COMBO PACK

– – – 18
$$$$

Digital Directory Assistance, Inc. Win/Mac/DOS
Phone Directories
This two-product pack contains the *PhoneDisc Business* and the *PhoneDisc Residential* products. Although it's a lot of listings, they're not integrated. Those who want business and residential data mixed together will be better off with one of the high-end phone books. For more information, see *Phone Disc Basic Information*.

PHONEDISC '95 POWERFINDER

21 – 19 19
$$$$$

Digital Directory Assistance, Inc. Win/Mac/DOS
Phone Directories
The top of the Digital Directory Assistance line, this product splits the country into five disks. The extra money invested in this set buys over 5 million additional residential listings and more search capabilities. The program can find and download listings by name, street address, city, state, zip, phone number or business classification. A well-liked feature of the "snappy," "easy-to-use" interface is that listings appear as search information is typed. For more information, see *Phone Disc Basic Information*.

PHONEDISC '95 RESIDENTIAL

– – – 18
$$

Digital Directory Assistance, Inc. Win/Mac/DOS
Phone Directories
This two-disc consumer product, contains over 80 million residential listings. Although listings can be downloaded, unlike the most expensive phone CDs, searches must start with the name, which can then be limited by city, state, zip or area code. No finding the name and phone number of the attractive person at 35 Main Street allowed. For more information, see *Phone Disc Basic Information*.

PICTURE ATLAS OF THE WORLD

16 18 18 **16**
$$$$

National Geographic Society, Educational Media   Win/Mac/DOS
Geography/Maps
Multimedia features may be "useless bells and whistles," but the information provided here "is crisp and clear." Descriptions of each country include photos, videos, flags, speech samples and the national music. A feature on maps and mapping is also included. Graphics and maps are supplemented with stats and essays, providing a more complete picture of how the world works This title is "particularly useful" for teens, "junior high" school students, and international explorers.

PICTURE PERFECT GOLF

17 17 14 **17**
$$

Lyriq International Corporation   DOS
Games/Sports Simulation
This title lacks the pizzazz of *Links386*. There's no golfer swinging the club, not even a ball to hit on most shots. Just swing the club and wait for the program to determine the lie. Scenery consists of digitized photos of actual courses, but the "washed-out" color doesn't salvage this "unsatisfying" program. While the current version requires a floppy disk for installation, Lyriq is preparing to release a Windows 95 version that installs from the CD-ROM.

PINBALL ILLUSIONS

– – –
$$

21st Century Entertainment, Inc.   DOS
Games/Parlor
While most games depart reality and zip off into the world of imagination, the makers of pinball sims traditionally boast of one thing—capturing the sounds and feel of the real thing. This multi-table package is no different, featuring the surfers of Babewatch, the bungee jumps of Extreme Sports, and the cyborg future cops of Law 'N' Justice. A multi-ball feature challenges pinball wizards to keep three balls in play at once.

PIZZA TYCOON

14 11 10 **13**
$$

MicroProse Software, Inc.   DOS
Games/Simulation
This new installment in the Tycoon series (the last was the popular *Transport Tycoon*, also reviewed here) puts the user in the "painfully real simulation" status of opening, managing and keeping a pizza shop in business. You'll choose menus and furniture, buy ingredients, manage your help and fend off thugs and Mafiosi, all while "repeatedly" slinging pizza, a prospect non-sim lovers can find "tedious and aggravating." Some people will do anything for the dough.

PLAN AHEAD FOR YOUR FINANCIAL FUTURE

18 15 19 **16**
$$
Win

Dow Jones & Company
Finance

Wall Street Journal reporters give "good advice" for people of any age making a retirement plan. Worksheets appear as you progress through the text and, when you finish, compute your financial goals. Video cameos from money experts introduce concepts like inflation, options for saving, and social security. Maybe there "isn't enough information here to fire your financial planner," but if you haven't got one, this is a good place to start on an important task.

PLANETARY TAXI

22 19 21 **20**
Ages: 9 & up $

Voyager Company
Science/Astronomy

Behind the wheel of an interplanetary checkered cab, passengers with great "voice characterization" challenge your knowledge of the solar system: 'Take me where my prize-winning pig weighs the most,' or 'Where's the nearest glass of water?' Collect tips, keep your mileage down, call dispatch for mission advice, or seek out the science facts you'll need to succeed. It's education in disguise—"great for teaching concepts of distance and space," though missions are limited.

PLAYBOY INTERVIEWS

20 12 18 **18**
$

IBM Multimedia Studio
Current Affairs
Win

WAIT! It's not what you think! No nudes, no femmes fatales...not even a cartoon. What there is is three decades of incredibly "interesting and enlightening" interviews. Hundreds of entries include such greats as Tennessee Williams musing about his art, John Lennon discussing his life, and Bill Cosby talking about race. Chock full of quotes, transcripts and audio clips, here's proof positive that Playboy did impact journalism, even if some of us "forgot just how good these interviews were."

PLAYROOM

17 18 19 **16**
Ages: 3-6 $$

Broderbund Software, Inc.
Kids/Early Learning Skills
Win/Mac

"Kids play for hours" with these six "well-designed" activities in the pioneer program that covers mountains of pre-school material. The Playroom is a simple place, with clickable animations and a coloring activity, but no glitzy multimedia. Easy enough for pre-schoolers to use, "they can be creative" while learning time-telling, counting and letter recognition. "Kids go back to it over and over and find new, fun things to do." "One great improvement from disk to CD-ROM."

POETRY IN MOTION

22 20 18 **19**

$

Voyager Company
Win/Mac
Literature

"Poetry as the poet intended" is the premise of Voyager's exquisitely done CD-ROM. Taken from a documentary, 24 poets, like William S. Burroughs, Allan Ginsberg and Tom Waits, read from their works Although the interface is "a bit clunky" and the title can wear thin after you view it once, it's "a good survey of current artists" and an "incredible opportunity" to experience the sensual world of the written word.

POLICE QUEST IV: OPEN SEASON

– – – **15**

Ages: 17 & up $$$

Sierra On-Line, Inc.
DOS
Games/Mystery

In one of the most unpleasant games around, your assignment is to find the maniac who tortured and killed your police detective partner. While finding clues is as simple as pointing and clicking, actually solving the mystery is a nightmare. ("This program is too complicated to be fun; it should come with the warning: For Police Officers Only.") The "realistic graphics" are practically of coroner quality. Has someone forgotten this is a game?

POLICE QUEST: THE FOUR MOST WANTED

19 14 13 **15**

$$$

Sierra On-Line, Inc.
Win/Mac
Games/Mystery

Correction: we cited *Police Quest IV* as the most unpleasant game on the shelves. The award belongs to this compilation of four earlier PQ mysteries. Players find it "gruesome, graphic, violent and bloody," appealing to some, a turn-off to others. Prepare to study the manual. Those who have played Sierra adventures before will find the genre very familiar. Novices should "be wary since the puzzles are tough and not very logical," though hints are included.

POPULAR MECHANICS NEW CAR BUYERS GUIDE 1995

19 17 19 **19**

$$

Books That Work
Win
Consumer Guides

If you've ever bought a new car, you know that searching showrooms doesn't mean you'll end up satisfied. This disc offers an alternative to smarmy salesmen, with a plus: users swear "it WILL save you money." An "exhaustive" title showing more than 800 new car makes and models, with buyers surveys, and details ranging from prices to leg room, this is an excellent CD-ROM car buying guide. "Don't buy a new car without this disc."

POWER JAPANESE

21 18 19 20

$$$$$

BayWare Inc. — Win

Language/Japanese

The Americans' need for Japanese-language proficiency has never been greater, and this title can help break the barrier. Users like the "well-organized" lessons in spoken and written Japanese, and find the audio pronunciation helpful. The online dictionary and word processor are useful tools. Some are overwhelmed by the emphasis on "active memorization" and underwhelmed by "good but unspectacular" graphics. Still, *Power Japanese* is considered one of the best of its kind.

POWER SPANISH

15 18 17 16

$$$$

BayWare Inc. — Win

Language/Spanish

Hola, estudiantes de Espanol! *Power Spanish*, a brightly colored jumble of graphics and soundbites, promises to provide the tools necessary to communicate in Spanish. Well, don't bet el rancho. This title proudly skimps on grammatical rules and tables, instead focusing on basic vocabulary and active verbs. This technique is more "abstract" than "practical," and while it'll certainly get you through a three-week trip to Acapulco; it won't get you through Spanish 101.

PREHISTORIA: A MULTIMEDIA WHO'S WHO OF PREHISTORIC LIFE

13 14 14 15

$$

Grolier Electronic Publishing, Inc. — Win

Kids/Science

Prehistoria offers an artist's glimpse of an array of land and sea animals from another era. The art is commendable, with life-like color and a keen attention to detail. The accompanying text, however, is prehistoric, with "more detail required to make this a top-notch CD." The lean use of audio and animation leaves you wondering, "What multimedia?" Better for dinosaur aficionados, who at least appreciate the difference between a plesiosaurus and a protoceratosaurus.

PRESIDENTS: A PICTURE HISTORY OF OUR NATION

15 9 12 12

$$$

National Geographic Society, Educational Media — DOS

History

This "mediocre" CD offers quick biographies on the first forty-one men (Bill Clinton is conspicuously missing) who have presided, along with facts about their eras, election processes and parties. Although it was rated high on content and as a "reference product," users rated multimedia and interactivity pickin's slim to none. Maybe it was the graphics. *The Presidents* has over a thousand pictures, but hides them in an interface that looks "plain."

129

	C	M	U	O

PRINCE INTERACTIVE
16 18 17 **17**

$$

Graphix Zone   Win/Mac
Music/Interactive Albums

Watch his videos. Listen to his music. Ponder his artistic vision. In this interactive exploration, users are invited to poke around an animated mansion belonging to the artist once known as Prince. While the *Myst*-like graphics are "breathtaking," some found the "egotistical" material overwhelming, and now that he's changed his name to a symbol, the hardest part of using this CD is figuring out what to call it. "A must for any serious Prince fan." *This is included in the 5 ft. 10 pak Collector's edition.*

PRINT ARTIST
19 19 20 **20**

Ages: 7 & up $$$

Maxis   Win
Graphics/Desktop Publishing

Make business cards, flyers, even banners from the comfort of your desktop. *Print Artist* gives you hundreds of customizable layouts to use when creating documents. With an "easy-to-use" interface and a "whopping" 2300 "colorful, hip" clip art images it's consistently praised for having "better" control over text and graphics than other home printing tools, but it's harder to create projects "from scratch." This is a "fun" way to ensure your prints are charming.

PRINT SHOP DELUXE CD ENSEMBLE
23 19 22 **22**

$$$$

Broderbund Software, Inc.   Win/Mac
Graphics/Desktop Publishing

Here's the "granddaddy" of home printing products, and it "just keeps getting better." This "great" program, created from five individual products, let's you create a huge variety of documents, from posters to business cards. The "plentiful" clip art is "incredible," and users rave "it has great features for adults," but even "elementary school age" kids can use it. One of the top choices for home printing.

PRINTMASTER GOLD CD BONUS PACK
18 17 20 **19**

$$$$

MicroLogic Software   Win
Graphics/Desktop Publishing

Users can create their own posters, banners, calendars and more ("great for making cards") with "near professional results." There are a variety of text, backgrounds, "mediocre" clip-art, fonts and tools. With a "remarkably helpful" audio tutor, this may be the "easiest" of the home publishing products, but with limits like an inability to import graphics, it has "fewer" features than its rivals. Overall, it's a "fun" title for the average home publisher. *A version without extra clip art and tools is in the 5 ft. 10 pak.*

PRO CD BASIC INFORMATION   − − −

Pro CD, Inc.
Phone Directories
After a while it seems "all phone directories are the same," but in fact each of the three major CD directories gets listings differently, and all shout they are best. Pro CD hires typists to enter some 6000 American phone directories. The result is nearly 100 million business and residential listings, updated quarterly, which include Names, Street Address, City, Zip+4, State, Business Classification (actually, over 2000 SIC codes), and Phone numbers. The data has surprisingly few obvious typos, but you're sure to find mistakes as this is messy work. Unpublished numbers (about one-third of all) are excluded. Finally, since 20% of phone listings change each year, if you need to be current, prepare to "update frequently."

PRO CD BUSINESS PHONE '96   − − − 18
$$
Pro CD, Inc.   Win/Mac/DOS
This single-disc lists 15 million businesses. Although listings can be downloaded, searches must start with the name or phone number, and afterwards can be further restricted by city, state, zip, area code or business classification. See *Pro CD Basic Information*.

PRO CD CANADA PHONE   − − − 18
$$$$$
Pro CD, Inc.   Win/Mac/DOS
This single-disk Canadian version of *SelectPhone* contains 12 million business and residential listings. The program can find and download listings by name, street address, city, province, postal code, phone number or business classification. See *Pro CD Basic Information*.

PRO CD DIRECT PHONE   21 − 20 20
$$$$
Pro CD, Inc.   Win/Mac/DOS
Discontinued and replaced by *Home & Business Phone '96*. See *Pro CD Basic Information*.

PRO CD FREE PHONE   15 − 18 15
$
Pro CD, Inc.   Win/Mac/DOS
Markets abhor a vacuum. Since business phone CDs skip toll free numbers, ProCD developed this single-disc to contain 250,000 entries directly from the tapes of the AT&T (not MCI or Sprint) 800-number directory. It's searchable by name, address, toll-free phone number and business type, but unsurprisingly "doesn't give the local phone number." By the way, many 800 numbers, including many tech support numbers, are unlisted. See *Pro CD Basic Information*.

PRO CD HOME & BUSINESS PHONE '96   –   –   –   18
$$$

Pro CD, Inc.   Win/Mac/DOS
This three-disk pack is a bundle containing *Home Phone '96* and *Business Phone '96*; see individual reviews. For additional information, see *Pro CD Basic Information*.

PRO CD HOME PHONE '96   19   –   21   19
$$

Pro CD, Inc.   Win/Mac/DOS
This two-disk consumer product, contains over 80 million residential listings. Although listings can be downloaded, unlike the most expensive phone CDs, searches must start with the name, which can then be limited by city, state, zip or area code. No finding the name and phone number of the attractive person at 35 Main Street allowed. For more information, see *Pro CD Basic Information*.

PRO CD SELECT PHONE, 1996 EDITION   –   –   –   19
$$$$$

Pro CD, Inc.   Win/Mac/DOS
The most expensive of the ProCD line, this "amazing" product splits the country into six disks. What you're paying for is powerful search capabilities; the program can find and download listings by name, street address, city, state, zip, phone number or business classification. Now you can find a long-lost friend and then telemarket his entire neighborhood. For more information, see *Pro CD Basic Information*.

PROFESSOR IRIS' FUN FIELD TRIP: ANIMAL SAFARI   14   18   15   12
Ages: 4 & up $$

Discovery Home Entertainment   Win/Mac
Kids/Edugames-Science
This user-friendly interactive CD storybook with learning activities retains a lot of its original TV flavor and fun. It offers "excellent" videos of the puppet cast and footage of Africa. The less enthused report "cute but so-so interface" and "not a lot of depth" or educational draw to all the games. But the dictionary of animal-related words is worthwhile and you can choose among English, French, Spanish or Japanese languages.

PUPPET MOTEL   20   20   17   19
$

Voyager Company   Mac
Avant Garde
This "interesting" and "enigmatic" collection of images and sounds produced by performance art queen Laurie Anderson is anything but typical. What appear to be random images on screen are actually part of a highly interactive multimedia presentation. But figuring the interface out can be "confusing" (hint: get familiar with the "escape" key). Nonetheless, if you appreciate "beautiful graphics" and "memorable stories," you'll probably get a kick out of this "CD for a snowy day."

PUTT-PUTT AND FATTY BEAR'S ACTIVITY PACK

21 21 19 **19**

Ages: 3-8 $

Humongous Entertainment Mac/DOS
Kids/Edugames-General

A set of 15 games, playable at a choice of three levels, this straightforward disc succeeds with solid quality and a simple format. Consisting mostly of old standbys like checkers, squares and word hunt, kids enjoy having the familiar characters Putt-Putt and Fatty Bear as guides and competitors. "Kids love this title," and with so many games to choose from, "they play for hours."

PUTT-PUTT GOES TO THE MOON

21 18 19 **19**

Ages: 3-7 $$

Humongous Entertainment Win/Mac/DOS
Kids/Edugames-General

Kids control the movements of the "irresistible" Putt-Putt, a friendly animated car, in his travels on the moon. Putt-Putt needs help finding pieces of the rocket that will take him home. Along the way there's lots of "fun exploration" in this auto hero's 1960s-style futuristic world—as well as minor detours to some games and puzzles. An "excellent children's game" that's "just the right challenge for 4- to 6-year-olds." No reading required.

PUTT-PUTT JOINS THE PARADE

20 20 20 **20**

Ages: 3-7 $$

Humongous Entertainment Win/Mac/DOS
Kids/Edugames-General

Young navigators steer Putt-Putt, the friendly animated car, on a scavenger hunt in Car Town. En route kids look for specific things, such as coins for a car wash, and help Putt-Putt earn money by performing tasks like mowing lawns. Then they figure out how many coins he needs for the car wash. With "less sophisticated" graphics than many titles, this is still a "wonderful kids' game" that's "stronger in entertainment than educational value." No reading required.

PUTT-PUTT SAVES THE ZOO

- - - **19**

Ages: 3-7 $$

Humongous Entertainment Win
Kids/Edugames-General

In this latest Putt-Putt, help find six missing baby animals by clicking Putt-Putt, the animated car, through the colorful Car Town zoo. There's plenty of exploring; click on little speakers to hear about natural animal habitats and collect objects that help save Kenya the lion cub and others. Pre-schoolers can't get enough of exploring with Putt-Putt, but since lost animals are in the same place every game, older kids are happy to solve things once. Great graphics make this a memory hog—better find 8 free meg.

QUARANTINE

16 17 16 **17**

$$

GameTek, Inc. — DOS
Games/Combat

A cabby who goes 90 miles an hour, aims at pedestrians, drives on sidewalks, and curses a lot…rush hour in New York City? Not exactly—you've also got guns out the side windows and roads booby-trapped with mines! Users are "pleasantly surprised" by this "fun game," which forces you to navigate a veritable obstacle course in order to "get out of a quarantined city" and deliver fares to chosen destinations. Ah, the life of a cabby…

QUARTERBACK ATTACK WITH MIKE DITKA

– – –

$$$

Digital Pictures Inc. — Mac/DOS
Games/Sports Simulation

Imagine you're a raw rookie quarterback and the starter goes down with a season-ending injury. All you have to do is run the offense the way the coach taught you. Thanks to a dynamic view from inside your own helmet, you see and hear everything, from receivers running patterns, to onrushing linebackers, and of course, Coach Ditka ripping you up one side and down the other after a blown play. What could be more fun?

QUICKEN DELUXE 4 FOR WINDOWS

23 20 21 **22**

$$$$

Intuit — Win
Finance

As the most popular home finance package, *Quicken* is "simply an excellent program." Users "rarely need the manuals" for this complete finance organization system. From creating budgets to paying bills, selecting mutual funds to preparing taxes, *Quicken* "has everything you need"—including video consultations by two professionals. The clean interface design is transparently intuitive, although Talking Tutor Yolanda is on hand to answer any questions. Paying the bills was never so much fun.

RAND MCNALLY CHILDREN'S ATLAS OF WORLD WILDLIFE

16 11 13 **12**

Ages: all $$

GameTek, Inc. — Win/Mac
Kids/Edugames-Science

With information on hundreds of animal species and their habitats, this is an "authoritative resource" on world wildlife. Information is easily accessible via an index or clickable maps, providing ways to look up specific entries as well as to browse, though the lack of hypertext links between entries limits exploration. While quite useful for school reports, its dull presentation, poor quality videos and mundane games won't keep kids coming back for more.

RAND MCNALLY QUICK REFERENCE ATLAS

- - - **15**

Ages: 10 & up $

Rand McNally New Media   Win/Mac

Geography/Maps

As its name implies, this title performs best as a quick reference for your 'where in the world' questions. The maps are well-presented, and a convenient place locator gets you to your destination quickly. However, this disc is mute and motionless, lacking all multimedia elements except text and graphics. There are reports from the field of memory problems during installation. Overall, this disc is no grand improvement over traditional print atlases.

RAND MCNALLY'S CHILDREN'S ATLAS OF THE UNITED STATES

- - - **17**

Ages: all $$

GameTek, Inc.   Win

Reference/Kids

Cram for a Kid's Quiz Show, or just enjoy scanning this six-game disc on U.S. geography, flora and fauna. Good detailed maps of the states are enhanced with photos and "fun" animations. Narrated text accompanies state histories and points of interest. A jigsaw puzzle of the states is "especially fun." This title could use "more text and videos," and a graphically appealing interface but it's still a good learning tool for kids ages 8–12.

RAND MCNALLY'S TRIPMAKER

20 17 19 **19**

$$$

Rand McNally New Media   Win

Travel/Maps & Atlases

After you enter start and end points *TripMaker* determines efficient routes and shows you attractions to visit en route. This "simple and elegant" trip planner is "not as good if you want to be told where to go," providing not much more than a list of some packaged tours. Look for improvements in the unreviewed '96 version—more map and itinerary detail and a new animated travel agent to suggest destinations based on your interests.

RANDOM HOUSE UNABRIDGED DICTIONARY, SECOND EDITION

19 17 19 **19**

$$$$

Random House New Media   Win/Mac/DOS

Reference/Dictionaries

For those who want a big unabridged CD-ROM dictionary, the 315,000 word *Random House* is a good choice. At well under $100, it's a bargain compared to the *Oxford English Dictionary* CD, and it includes 2200 illustrative drawings and 115,000 spoken pronunciations. Updated in 1993, it has modern lingo too. For around $20 additional, you can get a copy of the big hardcover book too.

RAVENLOFT: THE STONE PROPHET

16 16 15 **17**
$$$

Strategic Simulations Corporation — DOS
Games/Role-playing & Interactive Fiction
Wicked mummy-lord Anhktepot may be awakening and your group is trapped. Before he gets you, you must escape by finding the Stone Prophet wall. *Dungeons and Dragons* fans appreciate this "highly enjoyable" game, in which users create their own "fully-rounded" characters, choosing characteristics like race, gender and class. But it gets difficult fast and "graphics and sound could be better." That, plus a 90 page manual for openers, means this is not for the easily frustrated.

READ WITH ME 1 & 2

– – – **18**
Ages: 3-7 $$$

WordPerfect Corporation — Win
Kids/Edugames-Reading
This discontinued product will probably linger for a while, but look for price reductions. Five "well-designed" early reading activities include an animated alphabet video and matching, letter and word games. In Word Traveller, kids learn phonics by typing in letter combinations to make words that the program then pronounces. "Beautiful songs and rhythms," and well designed activity levels teaches "just what pre-readers need to know." Not the fanciest in town, but lots of "kid appeal."

READER RABBIT 1

18 18 21 **18**
Ages: 3-6 $$

The Learning Company — Win/Mac
Kids/Edugames-Reading
A revised "classic," this is the first, and many say the best, of a series. With graduated levels of difficulty, drill style activities work on simple word identification, spelling patterns, vocabulary and memory. Words and pictures are used to reinforce one another and engage early readers. It's "entertaining," "holds a child's attention" and helps with early reading. The focus is on learning, not interactive exploration, so "this will not captivate" unless kids have an interest in reading,

READER RABBIT 2

20 21 21 **21**
Ages: 5-8 $$

The Learning Company — Win/Mac
Kids/Edugames-Reading
A good follow-up to *Reader Rabbit 1*, these four graduated drill-type activities work on word building (about 1000 words), vowel sounds, word concepts (rhymes, homonyms, antonyms) and alphabetizing. Alphabet Dance, for example, requires you to alphabetize pairs of dancers; correct results are rewarded with a little jig. Well-designed, well-illustrated activities give solid drill and practice. This isn't the flashiest title around but it's educationally sound and "kids like it."

READER RABBIT 3

Ages: 6-9 $$

The Learning Company   Win/Mac

Kids/Edugames-Reading

Four "engaging" activities built around 200 paragraph-length mini-stories provide drill and practice in sentence structure. Kids classify phrases, select correctly ordered sentences, and fill in paragraph blanks. A hint system helps kids find correct answers. After kids complete a level, they can print out a customized newspaper. The "well-designed" graphics and sounds are "clever" at "effectively" presenting basic concepts of sentence structure. Good for both classroom and home use.

READER RABBIT'S INTERACTIVE READING JOURNEY

Ages: 3-7 $$$$

The Learning Company   Win/Mac

Kids/Edugames-Reading

Covering similar but expanded ground to *Reader Rabbits 1* and *2*, this "super journey" is based on the phonics curriculum developed in the Southwest Regional Laboratory. It combines 40 progressively challenging stories with well thought out drill and practice. Considered "excellent" despite "disappointment" with story content and complaints about the high price tag. This is "one of the best reading programs out there"—"motivating" to beginning readers.

READER RABBIT'S READING DEVELOPMENT LIBRARY, LEVEL 1

Ages: 5-7 $$

The Learning Company   Win/Mac

Kids/Edugames-Reading

Reader Rabbit is back with classic stories: The Three Little Pigs and Goldilocks and the Three Bears. Attractively produced with some clever twists, kids can read the stories themselves or hear them recounted from different points of view. Kids will be "fascinated" to hear the wolf's side of the pig's story. "Colorful" animations reinforce the storyline; "cheerful" music, "clever" sound effects and nice graphics make this a fun first reader.

READER RABBIT'S READING DEVELOPMENT LIBRARY, LEVEL 2

Ages: 5-7 $$

The Learning Company   Win/Mac

Kids/Edugames-Reading

Slightly more advanced than Level 1, this title retells two classic stories: Jack in the Beanstalk and City Mouse, Country Mouse, from the point of view of three different characters. The Beanstalk giant's musings, as he as asks "Fum! Fo! Fi! Fee! Why doesn't anyone think of me?" are sure kid-pleasers. Good graphics and animations, helpful word lists and appropriate activities, like matching words to pictures, round out this sweet and effective first reader.

READING BLASTER: INVASION OF THE WORD SNATCHERS

20 22 18 **20**

Ages: 7-10 $$

Davidson & Associates, Inc.   Win

Kids/Edugames-Reading

These "fun" and "addictive" activities include an arcade spelling game, an alphabetizing maze, a synonym/antonym identification game and two word puzzles. The interface "isn't intuitive," but get past that and the title is "entertaining." Its wide range of activities and skill levels will appeal to a variety of kids, especially ones who prefer action over a reading experience. *Reading Blaster* is "a joy," and helps make learning spelling and grammar less painful.

REBEL ASSAULT

17 21 19 **19**

$

LucasArts Entertainment Co.   Mac/DOS

Games/Combat

Using the ever-familiar *Star Wars* motif, this isn't your ordinary space shoot-out. You will get "meteor-sized goosebumps" from incredible sound effects of "Tie Fighters screaming by your ear." Although the majority of users found the game "challenging" and "tough to master," few thought of actually giving up on it. The game's many different sections "keep it from getting monotonous," and once past the training missions, "even a rookie can save the rebellion." *The first three levels are available in the LucasArts pack.*

REBEL ASSAULT II

- - -

$$$

LucasArts Entertainment Co.   Mac/DOS

Games/Combat

While moviegoers await the next installment in the *Star Wars* film series, they can temporarily satisfy their cravings with this follow-up to *Rebel Assault*. Like its enormously popular predecessor, it is a greatly enhanced experience, but this time, it features professional actors rather than animation. It combines hand-to-hand combat with flight simulation battle scenes as players fight to keep the Empire at bay. Be sure the Force is with you.

RECESS IN GREECE

21 20 19 **20**

Ages: 7-12 $

Morgan Interactive   Win/Mac

Kids/Edugames-Social Studies

Morgan, a cartoon chimp, is transported to ancient Greece and needs help getting home. This "fun" story, based on the Iliad, tracks his progress. Along the way, there are humorous educational animations and detours to seven games, some "much better" than others. One flaw: saving games causes exiting and some repetition on reloading. Hip lingo creates an irreverent romp, and kids may confuse myths and modern additions. "Where was this when I had to learn Greek Mythology?"

REDSHIFT

22 21 17 21

Ages: 11 & up $$$
Win/Mac/DOS

Maris Multimedia
Science/Astronomy

Learn astronomy with the help of this advanced CD-ROM. Although it skimps on graphics, sound and interaction, this is nevertheless a great title for astronomy amateurs and professionals. "The quality of *RedShift* is astronomical," supplying statistics, names, information and meticulous sky maps for countless objects, stars, constellations and planets. It's informative more than entertaining, and can get "so deep it's confusing," but you could use it "to stargaze forever."

REELECT JFK

14 19 13 15

$$

Compton's NewMedia
Win/Mac
Games/Mystery

This strategy game and whodunit drops you in the Oval Office after a failed assassination in Dallas and, boy, have you got troubles. Not only is the war raging, and demonstrators screaming about civil rights, but you keep getting these %$#! error messages. As JFK you try to get re-elected and also find your would-be-assassin. It's got impressive graphics and "really makes you think;" but also big flaws like too-little user "control" and a Cabinet of made-up characters.

RELENTLESS: TWINSEN'S ADVENTURE

22 23 22 22

$

Electronic Arts
DOS
Games/Role Playing & Interactive Fiction

Our hero, Twinsen, is a member of the quetch race hailing from the fantasy planet Twinsun, and his mission is to rescue his people from the nefarious Dr. Funfrock. The "brilliant interface" makes helping him relatively easy. You just assign Twinsen a mood and move him toward his task. So, for example, when he needs to attack you make him aggressive. "Cutesy," "cheerful" 3-D graphics and "awesome animation" help make *Relentless* "original" and "fun."

RENEGADE

18 19 14 16

$$$

Strategic Simulations Corporation
DOS
Games/Combat

"A rip-off of *Wing Commander*" that's "not as good as the original," but the state-of-the-art graphics are almost worth the price alone. Even role players will be impressed as correct choices must be made if your pilot is to make it back into the Legion—what ships will be flown, who should fly them, what weapons will be needed? You've plenty of time to ponder: "mission loading times can stretch into minutes."

C M U O

RETURN TO ZORK
20 20 18 **19**

$$$

Activision   Mac/DOS
Games/Role Playing & Interactive Fiction
If you enjoyed any of the *Zork* games in the 1980s, this clas-
sic adventure game will probably bring back "wonderful
memories." With the aid of a kindly wizard, players solve
puzzles to stop a plot to destroy the human race. The video
tends to get "grainy" and the interface can be "somewhat
clunky," but the whole package is "just as fun as the origi-
nal" and will please any adventure game buff.

RIPPER
– – –

$$$$

Take 2 Interactive Software, Inc.   Mac/DOS
Games/Role Playing & Interactive Fiction
How far is too far when it comes to computer game vio-
lence and gore? There's sure to be such discussion after the
release of this one, an ambitious four-CD extravaganza
starring Christopher Walken, Karen Allen, Burgess Mered-
ith, Ossie Davis and Jimmie Walker. Jack the Ripper is
back, this time on the streets of Manhattan. His trail leads
from cyberspace to the comatose mind of his latest victim
where players find they're next on his hit list.

RISE OF THE ROBOTS
12 22 11 **12**

$$$

Time-Warner Interactive Group   DOS
Games/Combat
Although the graphics and animation in this game are
impressive, they simply do not make up for the title's lack
of content. "There's no plot!" complain users. "You battle
robots, but you don't even know exactly why." Players
have to beat five robots before facing the main villain—
a waif-like morphing robot called a Supervisor. Once there,
the game is over, and the user is left wondering 'why?'

RISE OF THE TRIAD
17 17 17 **17**

Ages: 13 & up $

Apogee Software   Win/DOS
Games/Combat
Choose one of five commandos, give 'em a gun and blast
your way through a labyrinth that contains 28 danger-
filled levels crammed with intricate graphics. Realistic
sound effects and an energizing score combine for ultra-
realism. While some may find its graphic violence "too
nasty," parents appreciate the violence-level adjustment.
Features include modem play and being able to "look up
and down, bounce off trampolines and turn into a dog."
Now that's unique!

ROCK 'N' ROLL YOUR OWN

16 19 17 **18**
$

Compton's NewMedia   Win/Mac
Music/Appreciation

Okay, so it doesn't "come close" to "professional" sound. Still, *Rock 'N' Roll Your Own* puts you in the studio, and lets you "soup up" riffs and bridges to make "killer" rock. You can work with eight songs, rearranging licks and wahs, and even make an "MTV-style" video. Or, use the "slick interface" to click your way to a more personal musical genius. Even users with "little musical experience" can recreate Warren Zevon's "Werewolves in London" like a highly-paid producer. Rock On.

ROMEO & JULIET

20 15 17 **17**
$

Attica Cybernetics Ltd.   Win
Literature

For never was a story of more woe brought to life on your PC. This title helps users "get a handle" on the Bard, from simply enjoying the story to enhancing your "understanding" of the language and meaning. Audio performances, video highlights, background information and language guides accompany scrolling text screens in a "classy" interface. The BBC performance is "excellent," although limited and "somewhat garbled." A "good resource" for fans and scholars alike.

ROSETTA STONE ENGLISH, LEVEL IA

16 14 16 **16**
$$$$$

Fairfield Language Technologies   Win/Mac
Language/English

If you've ever used flashcards or a language lab, you'll be familiar with the technique used in the *Rosetta Stone* series. These extensive CD sets each have 92 chapters that teach language by 'immersion.' Learning is by association and trial and error so students sees pictures along with the written word or phrase and also hear it pronounced. "Definitely not a slick multimedia program," but *Rosetta Stone* has "good" emphasis on "spoken AND written" language. Lessons proceed from listening to reading comprehension, then to speaking and writing. The Russian title is the first, and best, of the series.

ROSETTA STONE ESPANOL, LEVEL IA

18 17 18 **18**
$$$$$

Fairfield Language Technologies   Win/Mac
Language/Spanish
See *Rosetta Stone English.*

ROSETTA STONE FRANCAIS, LEVEL IA

18	17	18	**18**

$$$$

Fairfield Language Technologies — Win/Mac
Language/French
See *Rosetta Stone English.*

ROSETTA STONE RUSSIAN, LEVEL IA

19	19	19	**19**

$$$$

Fairfield Language Technologies — Win/Mac
Language/Russian
See *Rosetta Stone English.*

ROYAL FLUSH

19	22	16	**16**

$$

Amtex Software Corporation — DOS
Games/Parlor

While most pinball programs serve up multiple boards, this lovingly recreates just one classic table—but what a recreation. "This is as realistic as computer pinball gets," with photorealistic gameplay and sounds that exactly mimic the 1976 favorite. Start right up or tweak the table to your heart's content—adjust the incline, the tilt sensitivity, or the voltage. But first set aside some time to tweak those configuration files to get this one cranking.

RUFF'S BONE

20	22	21	**20**

Ages: 3-8 $$

Living Books — Win/Mac
Kids/Stories

Part of the Living Books series, this is a story of a dog's search for the bone his owner throws for him, and his adventures along the way. Words are highlighted and there are many clickable animations. A "big plus" is being able to hear it in Spanish. Despite the fact that it's "slow" turning between pages, and in Read-to-Me mode you have to hear an entire narration before being able to activate animations, this is a "fun story," even if it is not one of the best Living Books.

SAFARI

19	21	18	**19**

$$

Medio Multimedia Inc. — Win
Science/Animals

Safari is a peaceful and colorful romp through the Masai Mara and Serengeti National Parks with award-winning wild-life photographer Jonathan Scott. Explore the contents on your own or choose one of eleven beautifully-narrated guided tours. Set in a simple interface, the "stunning photography," the "beautiful—if somewhat grisly—video" and the 79 audio tracks of exotic animal sounds will entertain you for hours. This is natural history à la PBS.

SAM & MAX HIT THE ROAD
20 16 20 **20**
$

LucasArts Entertainment Co.   Mac/DOS
Games/Role Playing & Interactive Fiction
Based on the comic book *Sam & Max, Freelance Police*. Sam, a canine detective dressed in "a cheap suit" and Max, a bunny who revels in gratuitous acts of violence and is constantly in search of a bathroom, are trying to "find a carnival's missing bigfoot, but who cares?" The "irreverent," warped adult humor and animation that "rings of '60s underground comics" make this a "ton of fun." A simple interface means it's a breeze to manipulate the characters. *This game is included in the LucasArts pack.*

SAMMY'S SCIENCE HOUSE
21 21 22 **21**
Ages: 2-5 $$

Edmark Corporation   Win/Mac/DOS
Kids/Edugames-Science
These enjoyable logic and science activities "pull your toddler through the screen into a fun and educational world." The Puzzle Maker, Film Sequencer and Animal Sorting are favorites. A good mixture of creative and rote response activities makes this title "a winner," offering "some fun new ways" to engage your child's mind. Help is provided in clever ways, keeping little ones on course. By the way, "check out Sammy the Snake's parody of the MGM lion."

SAN DIEGO ZOO PRESENTS... THE ANIMALS! VERSION 2.0
21 22 21 **21**
Ages: 8 & up $$

Mindscape   Win/Mac
Kids/Science
A "wonderful kid-level introduction" to the world of animals, this is a rare mix of fun and learning. Like any great visit to the zoo, *The Animals* fosters a sense of discovery, adventure and humor. Kids travel to 10 exhibit areas profiling 202 animals with short articles, photos and usually a video or audio clip. 'Story Theater' offers 14 interesting slide shows on zoo topics like 'Feeding at the Zoo.' "A must for anyone with children."

SATURDAY NIGHT LIVE: THE FIRST TWENTY YEARS
14 14 12 **13**
$

GameTek, Inc.   Win/Mac
Humor
Comprised mostly of video footage from the best SNL skits of the last twenty years, this two-disc CD-ROM set keeps you laughing—at least the first time through. Featuring such favorites as The Blues Brothers, Weekend Update, and Presidential Impersonations, it's "great if you are an SNL buff." Alas, most feel it "does very little to enhance the raw material" and that "after initial perusal, it will likely double as a drink coaster."

C M U **O**

SAVAGE WARRIORS
– – –

Mindscape $$
Games/Combat DOS

Tired of kicking, punching and jumping through *Mortal Kombat*, *MK II* and *MK III*? You may want to take a break—and kick, punch and jump your way through *Savage Warriors*, described as grueling combat on a distant island with the fiercest warriors in human history. Whew! There are a dozen heroes, a slew of animated backgrounds, and a bunch of deadly weapons from which to choose. If you're wondering whether to look for cheat modes, there are 20 of 'em.

SCIENCE SLEUTHS, VOLUME 1
20 19 19 **20**
Ages: 12 & up $$

Videodiscovery, Inc. Win/Mac
Kids/Science

Sift through multimedia clues to solve the mysteries of The Blob, and The Exploding Lawnmowers. A clean and sophisticated interface uses a cheeky head investigator to give assignments and confirm findings. The clever lab tools let you conduct a variety of scientific tests on samples from the scene. With a choice of six levels of increasing difficulty, this disc "turns science learning into a detective story," entertaining adults and children alike. Too bad there are only two mysteries to solve.

SCIENCE SLEUTHS, VOLUME 2
20 19 19 **19**
Ages: 12 & up $$

Videodiscovery, Inc. Win/Mac
Kids/Science

Duplicating Volume 1's format, this is another "fun way to experiment" with two entertaining science investigations: The Mysteries of The Biogene Picnic and The Traffic Accident. Maps, graphs, documents, video, lab tools, and a database all hold clues to solving the mystery. Hints are available when you need them. The Notebook feature allows you to record information collected and reach conclusions. If only there were more than two mysteries here.

SCOOTER'S MAGIC CASTLE
19 19 21 **19**
Ages: 5-8 $$

Creative Wonders DOS
Kids/Stories

Colorful graphics and an easy interface help make this "one of the better children's titles" available. *Home Improvement's* Jonathan Taylor Thomas plays the voice of Scooter, your guide through three floors of fully interactive "exploratory fun." Lessons are hidden inside over 20 engaging games, teaching memory, color, and creativity. The "excellent" graphics and fun things to do will have kids from four to seven coming back to the *Magic Castle*.

SELECT PHONE, 1996 EDITION

$$$$$

See *Pro CD Select Phone, 1996 Edition.*

SESAME STREET: LET'S MAKE A WORD

Ages: 3-6 $$

Creative Wonders Win
Kids/Edugames-Spelling

The slickest of the *Sesame Street* CD-ROM titles, six games, with good character interaction, are presented in a game-show format. Reading readiness is covered from first letter sounds to sounding out whole words. Kids can also learn words in Spanish. The game show host has surprisingly varied lines and the games are "entertaining enough to hold even a three-year-old's attention," while the solid content will help youngsters on the path to reading.

SESAME STREET: LETTERS

Ages: 3-6 $$

Creative Wonders Win/Mac/DOS
Kids/Early Learning Skills

"As reliable as the show," this pre-reading title lets kids explore by moving a star-shaped cursor that sparkles on objects that hold clickable "fun" surprises. While visiting homes of three characters, kids can watch real TV clips from the *Sesame Street* show and play letter games. There's a telephone for chatting with "all the Sesame Street regulars." Not as sophisticated as the *Sesame Street Lets Make a Word*, but still good pre-school fun.

SESAME STREET: NUMBERS

Ages: 3-6 $$

Creative Wonders Mac/DOS
Kids/Edugames-Math

The familiar *Sesame Street* gang is "encouraging and engaging," making this otherwise unexceptional title enjoyable. There are four, mostly numeric, games and a few interactive elements, such as a cartoon TV with brief video clips from the show. The "grainy" graphics and "difficult to learn" games make it less engaging than the other *Sesame Street* titles. Nonetheless, kids love the "music and voices of the characters" and, with assistance, enjoy the games.

SHADOWS OF CAIRN

$

Masque Publishing Win/Mac/DOS
Games/Role Playing & Interactive Fiction

Combining adventure and action, this game succeeds at neither. The user controls Quinn, a minuscule figure who must solve puzzles in order to prevent the assassination of the Duke of Cairn. Many found the graphics "a delight," and said the game "sounds great," but the "frustrating" interface responds slowly and Quinn's actions are limited to basic back-and-forth movements. Until these issues are solved, this one will remain lost in the shadows.

SHANGHAI: GREAT MOMENTS

19 18 16 **19**

$

Activision Win
Games/Parlor

Nothing has made office productivity suffer more than *Tetris* and *Shanghai*. The latter, a mindless diversion of tile-matching and removal, gets the "full multimedia treatment" as each match turns into a mini-video. While the original game was challenging enough, some of the newer varieties here—particularly one in which tiles are added every few seconds—are "unbelievable." Best played on a Pentium where the endless pauses will seem less like the slow boat to China.

SHARKS!

18 17 18 **17**

Ages: 8 & up $

Discovery Home Entertainment Win/Mac
Science/General

From the safety of your ocean-going submersible, explore the natural history and cultural influences of these fascinating creatures. Thirty minutes of "rather dramatic" video includes interviews with shark bite survivors complete with "rather gross" pictures of the bites. But while it's filled with interesting information, it's too passive—kids want "more activities" to engage their interest. A good reference for in-school use, "without activities," it's not likely to resurface much at home.

SHERLOCK HOLMES, CONSULTING DETECTIVE, VOLUMES I–III

20 12 15 **16**

$

Viacom Interactive Media Mac/DOS
Games/Mystery

Elementary, my dear Watson! These CD's are "faithful" to the mind-twisting cases of Arthur Conan Doyle. Each volume gives users a set of three mysteries to solve. After correctly answering a quiz on each mystery, Holmes appears via video to go over the case. Although the multimedia isn't overwhelming, the video clips are "interesting." *Consulting Detective* is a stumper that entertains mystery buffs as it puzzles them. Parts available in the *5 Ft., 10 Pak*; Volumes I–III are also available bundled together.

SILVER PLATTER COOKBOOK

16 11 18 **16**

See *MasterCook Silver Platter Cookbook*.

SIMCITY 2000

Ages: 11 & up $$$

Maxis   Win/Mac/DOS

Games/Simulation

Crime's up, pollution's choking the air, and a tornado's heading your way. And you thought ruling SimCity would be a snap ("If my kids can do it, I'm not giving up."). First you need to get through the manual. Then the real challenge is self-control ("It's 2 AM and I have work in the morning—help!"). "Don't buy" this "addictive" title "unless you are willing to be sucked in for days, months, years."

SIMPLY 3D

$$$

Visual Software   Win

Graphics/Desktop Publishing

Have you ever wondered how graphic designers get ads to look so realistic? Well, this title lets you create your own slick visuals. Split into a number of different programs, *Simply 3D* allows users to manipulate text, graphics and clip-art so that they look vibrant and three-dimensional. Although novices find it "hard to use," this program ultimately does have a "friendly" interface that "gets easier as you work with it."

SIMPLY HOUSE

$$$

4Home Productions   Win

House and Garden

In this title the house is "the user interface." Roam a nice suburban ranch, clicking on items that interest you. Up pops a "nice reference" based on the *Stanley Complete Step-by-Step Home Repair Guide*. There's "lots of solid information," and the "navigational interface" is pretty cool, but there could be more video. And not everything is there—for example, garbage disposals are tough to find. Not bad, not great, *Simply House* is simply fair.

SIMTOWER

$$

Maxis   Win/Mac

Games/Simulation

Now you can own your personal skyscraper "with no liability." Though it is slower, "less ambitious" and lacks the "rich detail" of its extremely popular predecessor, *SimCity*, this game is still engaging. You must create a functioning, profitable building by keeping tenants happy (that's a game?), overseeing maintenance, adjusting rent, building facilities and keeping day-to-day stuff in check. Make sure you have time on your hands—and profits on your mind—before picking this one up.

SIMTOWN

20 21 18 **20**

Ages: 8-12 $$

Maxis Mac

Games/Simulation

SimCity and *SimCity 2000* were meant for adults longing for omnipotence, but they also became "favorite programs" for teens. Now, younger kids can get into a kinder, gentler building act, with this "really interactive" CD. One major flaw is that *SimTown* is "slow," yes, "really slow." "More instructions" would help little users, but the graphics are excellent, and kids like that it's "hands-on" and there's "a lot of things you could do."

SKIER'S ENCYCLOPEDIA

12 16 18 **12**

$$

Romboy Win

Sports Reference

This disc offers a comprehensive list of 400 ski-resorts, widely searchable by such things as location and elevation. It's got a section on equipment, and "sound," easy-to-follow video ski lessons covering topics like stance, pole use, steering and skiing on steep trails, moguls, powder and ice. It could be great, but resort trail maps are "hard to read," smaller resorts are given short shrift and there are "no photos." Also, the equipment section is mostly "promotional videos."

SLAM CITY WITH SCOTTIE PIPPIN

14 21 14 **14**

$$$

Digital Pictures Inc. DOS

Games/Sports Simulation

This four-CD interactive basketball game features "spectacular" interactive video and excellent sound effects, though some say the writing and acting are "deplorable." Executing difficult moves earns respect points, and the privilege of playing tougher opponents. Player control is sometimes shaky, and most find the gameplay "limited," but the challenge of facing Scottie Pippen will probably keep you driving the lane. The most important move is getting a fast, ideally Pentium, machine.

SMALL BLUE PLANET: THE CITIES BELOW

18 17 18 **17**

Ages: 12 & up $$

Cambrix Publishing Win/Mac

Geography/Maps

"Stunning photo-realistic" aerial maps of America's biggest cities make this title "just plain cool." Zoom toward earth for a bird's-eye view, through satellite images, of your chosen city. But since it only includes major cities, "god help you if you're from the midwest." There's almanac information good for such things as learning about the evolution of cities, though some cite "poorly written" text. Others say the lack of sound and video means this isn't "a true urban experience."

SMALL BLUE PLANET: THE REAL PICTURE WORLD ATLAS

20 18 17 **18**
$$
Cambrix Publishing   Win/Mac
Geography/Maps

Ever put your ear to a map? Well, this one's got something to say. With 15 expressions recited in 70 languages, there's also "tons and tons" of information on the landscape, economy, politics and environmental issues of all the countries of the world. And of course there's the "cool" satellite images, though they "only zoom in so far." Despite "mysterious" tool icons that create some confusion, you're likely to spend "hours and hours with this one."

SMITHSONIAN'S AMERICA

17 19 19 **18**
$$
Creative Multimedia Corporation   Win
History

Based on a 1994 exhibit in Japan, this tour of American culture and history contains a "rich archive" of photos, videos, documents and narration. Organized by topics such as 'The Peopling of America' and 'Politics and Protest,' there are photo slide shows, artifacts galleries—with objects from the Smithsonian's collection—and a timeline. Long-winded narrations that you can't exit and a "limited" view of our "multicultural" history are weak spots in this "entertaining," "informative" CD.

SOMEBODY CATCH MY HOMEWORK

19 12 17 **18**
Ages: 7 & up $
Discis Knowledge Research, Inc.   Win/Mac
Kids/Stories & Poems

David Harrison's poetry is "fun" and "humorous," capturing "timeless" childhood dilemmas in a winsome, "appealing" way. Other features add "educational value," from "lively narration" to word pronunciation, definitions and Spanish translations. The interview with the author is a nice, inspiring touch. However, the use of the original illustrations from his book, although lovely, does not create the "high impact" visual punch your kids might be looking for.

SOUND IT OUT LAND 1

20 16 18 **19**
Ages: 4-6 $$
Conexus, Inc.   Win
Kids/Edugames-Reading

The first in a series, this title teaches letter sounds and short words for kids who already know the alphabet. Children like the "catchy" songs and parents find this title helps three- and four-year-olds learn to read, even though it's basically "an interactive flashcard." The activities take place in an amusement park. As they visit different attractions, kids sound out letters and match them to pictures. It's good drill and practice, even though it gets "stale" with continued use.

SOUND IT OUT LAND 2

21 18 18 **19**

Ages: 4-6 $$

Conexus, Inc.   Win

Kids/Edugames-Reading

The second in the *Sound It Out Land* series, this title moves on to the next level in reading by working on blended consonant and vowel sounds as well as short sentences. Otherwise it's the same as its predecessor, with the same four characters and basic activities. See review of *Sound It Out Land 1*.

SOUND IT OUT LAND 3

- - - **18**

Ages: 4-6 $$

Conexus, Inc.   Win

Kids/Edugames-Reading

The third in a series, this title moves on to the next level in reading by working on the silent 'e' rule, three letter sound combinations and longer words. Otherwise, it's the same as its two predecessors, with the same four characters and basic activities. See review of *Sound It Out Land 1*.

SOUTHERN LIVING COOKBOOK

- - - **15**

$

Lifestyle Software Group   Win

Cooking & Food

Need peach pie for the fair? Start here. Bulging with 1600 recipes from *Southern Living* magazine, and a heavy-duty search facility, you will find recipes in almost any imaginable way—name, ingredients, difficulty—but not nutritionally. Reviewers like the 100 narrated photos and videos, showing "ins and outs" of techniques like cake decorating, but want more than "only 400 photos" for 1600 recipes. Still, this popular title will keep recipe collectors "addicted."

SPANISH NOW!

21 17 20 **20**

$$$$

Transparent Language   Win/Mac

Language/Spanish

See *Transparent Language Now! Series*.

SPELLBOUND!

20 15 19 **18**

See *Super Solvers Spellbound!*.

SPELLING JUNGLE

21 19 19 **21**

Ages: 7-10 $$

Sierra On-Line, Inc.   Win/Mac

Kids/Edugames-Spelling

This arcade spelling game features a guru/wizard character as guide on a trip up river. Along the way, kids gather letters, using them to spell words to get past obstacles. The guide, with his parrot perched on his finger, and the various sound effects are "entertaining." While it's a simple game without much variation or interaction, kids "love it" and find it a "most enjoyable" way to learn spelling.

150

SPIDER-MAN CARTOON MAKER

18 16 17 **18**

Ages: 5 & up $$

Knowledge Adventure   Win

Kids/Art & Writing

If you've ever felt like being in charge of an animated cartoon, this is for you. It's "easy-to-use," and relies on a wide variety of stock images, sounds, animations and backgrounds to put kids in control of their favorite overgrown arachnid. The disc receives praise for its "interactivity" and ability to "create your own characters and settings." It's also one of the few that lets kids animate every step of a cartoon—instead of watching the program do it.

SPORTS ILLUSTRATED FOR KIDS

19 19 17 **19**

See *Everything You Want To Know About Sports Encyclopedia*.

SPORTS ILLUSTRATED MULTIMEDIA ALMANAC, 1995 EDITION

21 19 17 **19**

$$

StarPress Multimedia   Win/Mac

Sports Reference

This title packs in a year's worth of *Sports Illustrated* issues, the *SI 1995 Sports Almanac*, and lots of photos and videos. Select a particular issue by clicking on its cover or one of 18 sports to get all the pertinent data. Browse the "well stocked" multimedia gallery, look at stats, and test your knowledge with a trivia quiz. Text and multimedia is "on par with the SI name," but the absence of hyperlinking makes it "rather frustrating to sift through" all the images.

SPORTS ILLUSTRATED SWIMSUIT CALENDAR

10 8 10 **11**

$

Softkey International   Win

Graphics/Desktop Publishing

For those who are so inclined, there are better ways to see women in skimpy bikinis. Users can create their own personalized Playboy-style calendars, but the interface is a major "hassle." The calendar portion is "useful enough," but many competing programs do it better. The scantily-clad models look great, but lack "warmth" and "don't seem real." You're better off buying a wall calendar and marking when the Swimsuit issue is ready for unwrapping.

STAR TRAIL

19 18 18 **20**

$$$$

Sir-Tech Software   DOS

Games/Role Playing & Interactive Fiction

The "interface is easy," but that's about all in this nonetheless well-liked role-playing game. Not a beginner's title, but well-seasoned role players enjoy playing almost any character imaginable in this Tolkienesque quest for the Salamander Stone. Choose from 12 classes of races and 52 different skills, and then arm yourself from a list of 350 types of weapons and 80 spells. Hey, whatever happened to just a good ol' sword and shield?

STAR TREK 25TH ANNIVERSARY

19 14 14 **14**
$$

Interplay Productions   Mac/DOS
Games/Puzzle & Logic

Boldly go where no CD-ROM has gone before... well, almost. Although this adventure game has some camp value, its multimedia could use a Dilithium crystal boost. Just "click on every part of the screen to find things you need," and then put them together in the correct order. One nice feature is the use of original voices, like William Shatner's and Leonard Nimoy's. But with only "fair" graphics and puzzles, there aren't enough "thinking" activities for this game to either live long or prosper.

STAR TREK: THE NEXT GENERATION "A FINAL UNITY"

16 21 19 **19**
$$$

Spectrum Holobyte, Inc.   DOS
Games/Role Playing & Interactive Fiction

Beam aboard the Starship Enterprise and immerse yourself in an episode of *Star Trek: The Next Generation*. Become captain Jean-Luc Picard and direct the action, making decisions while the crew of the Enterprise works to save the Federation from disaster. Digitized animations are basic but "excellent." The game itself is fun to operate. For trekkies from ages past, as well as the newly converted, this is "just like being a member of the crew."

STAR TREK: THE NEXT GENERATION INTERACTIVE TECHNICAL MANUAL

21 21 19 **19**
$$

Simon & Schuster Interactive   Win/Mac
Games/Role Playing & Interactive Fiction

Explore the U.S.S. Enterprise as never before with Quick Time VR, a feature that makes this title "a stand out." Relying on 15,000 photos, it gives you "360-degree photographic views" as you move your mouse to inspect every corner of the vessel. Despite drawbacks—the title "requires too much memory" and is low on interactivity, Trekkies are like kids loose in a candy store—they examine every nook and cranny of the space ship and eat it up.

STEPHEN BIESTY'S INCREDIBLE CROSS-SECTIONS STOWAWAY

23 17 18 **21**
Ages: 10 & up $

Dorling Kindersley Publishing, Inc.   Win/Mac/DOS
Kids/Science

How did things worked before the age of technology? This "must-have" title takes you to the scene with real firsthand close-ups. Examine an 18th-century warship through "very interesting" narration, great graphics and witty animations. Learn about sailors who collected rainwater in order to wash their clothes, and sick crew members who pretended to be healthy so they would not lose their portion of grog! This title is a thumbs-up..."one to be matched against others."

STEPHEN HAWKING'S A BRIEF HISTORY OF TIME

22 13 16 **17**

Ages: 14 & up $$
Creative Labs   Win/Mac
Science/Astronomy

This electronic edition of Hawking's best-selling book is a novel presentation of "ideas worth understanding" and "does a good job of making complex concepts easier to grasp." The art design is bold and innovative, and an ethereal sound track accompanies Hawking's synthesized voice. However, the much-touted Hawking Craft is confusing to navigate and the disc lacks enough interactivity to justify its CD reincarnation.

STICKYBEAR PRESCHOOL

— — — **9**

Ages: 2-6 $$
Optimum Resource, Inc.   DOS
Kids/Early Learning Skills

This program misses its target audience because it's "too hard for toddlers" to use and too "simple" a design to keep older kids interested. Though *Stickybear* offers "good content" with exercises in numbers, shapes and the alphabet, the "use of keys was very confusing." So, despite good educational value, this is an early learning program without an audience.

STORYBOOK MAKER

15 17 17 **16**

Ages: 5-8 $$$
Jostens Home Learning   Win/Mac
Kids/Art & Writing

Here's a creative writing package that provides the elements for kids to illustrate their own stories, including backgrounds, art tools and stickers. Kids can record and add their own voices and choose from an assortment of sound effects as well. Its primary advantage: it's easy to use for very young writers. But overall, it's "not as good as other storybook making programs."

STORYBOOK WEAVER DELUXE

23 22 21 **21**

Ages: 6-12 $$$
MECC   Win/Mac
Kids/Art & Writing

Create and illustrate stories in English or Spanish. "Excellent for encouraging writing and creativity," this title has "great versatility" and an "amazing" text-to-speech component. With its "splendid" printing, it "will motivate you to buy a color printer" if you don't already have one. A better image search tool would be useful since "it takes a long time" to scroll through picture elements. Nonetheless, this is a "super" and enjoyable creative writing tool.

STOWAWAY!

23 17 18 **21**

See *Stephen Biesty's Incredible Cross-Section Stowaway!*.

STRADIWACKIUS: THE COUNTING CONCERT

17 19 16 16

Ages: 5 & up $

T/Maker Win/Mac

Kids/Music

Enjoy a multi-lingual exploration of musical instruments and numbers with 10 pages, each featuring a different instrument, and accessible activities, such as creating an eight-note scale. Adults "are attracted by the music," and appreciate the "delightful graphics" and subject matter. A "fun title" for some kids, others find it "too easy" and get "bored in 15 minutes." The music/math relationship is one worth exploring, but this presentation is "lacking features" to hold kids' interest.

STREET ATLAS USA 2.0

21 16 19 20

$$$$

DeLorme Mapping Systems Win

Travel/Maps & Atlases

A "wonderful" mapping program, containing just about every U.S. road, it can be magnified until you're looking at just a few square blocks. Find maps by clicking an area or inputting zip code, city name or phone number. The "redraw is slow," and there are errors and outdated information, such as university names that "changed over 30 years ago." It's still a "tremendously precise" navigation tool that's "fun to use" and puts the "entire U.S. in your pocket."

STUDENT WRITING & RESEARCH CENTER

- - - 21

Ages: 10 & up $$$$

The Learning Company Win

Kids/Art & Writing

A pumped-up *Student Writing Center* with all the writing tools of the original, plus *Compton's Concise Encyclopedia*. The built-in encyclopedia is pared down from the well-known *Compton's*, with most of the multimedia, but less text and fewer features. Having a word processor and encyclopedia handy might make it easy for kids to craft slick-looking reports fast. But this disc costs more than *Student Writing Center*, and older kids will need more information for reports with any depth.

STUDENT WRITING CENTER

23 20 22 22

Ages: 10 & up $$$

The Learning Company Win

Kids/Art & Writing

This valuable program makes simple work of constructing correct writing formats. There are templates for reports, newsletters, signs, journals, letters and more, plus useful tips on content and style for each document type, bibliographic formatting, and a large, handy picture library for illustrating documents. A "fantastic collection of clip art… plenty of fonts," and a "terrific" word processor combined with an "easy to use" platform to make a "wonderful" tool for middle- and high-school students.

SUNSET WESTERN GARDEN
20 15 22 **17**

See *Western Garden.*

SUPER SOLVERS GIZMOS & GADGETS!
21 18 22 **22**

Ages: 7-12 $$

The Learning Company
Win/Mac

Kids/Edugames-Science

Locked doors and roaming monkeys hide parts needed to assemble each of 15 vehicles. Parts are found by solving science problems, and when vehicles are assembled the best possible way, players advance in rank. Thoroughly engrossing at first, parents may have to "pry" their kids "off the computer." Despite its unspectacular graphics, *Gizmos & Gadgets* has good design and "solid" content that engages scientifically-inclined kids.

SUPER SOLVERS OUTNUMBERED!
- - - **17**

Ages: 7-10 $$

The Learning Company
Win/Mac

Kids/Edugames-Math

While searching for the Master of Mischief in a TV station, kids solve math problems and practice math facts. Problems get harder as kids win games and parents can customize level of difficulty and type of problems. The math word problems, which often include charts, are great for reading comprehension. Though the same basic game is repeated with different problems, the "action is fast and fun."

SUPER SOLVERS SPELLBOUND!
20 15 19 **18**

Ages: 7-12 $$

The Learning Company
Win/Mac

Kids/Edugames-Spelling

Kids learn to spell 1000 words in four "amusing" games. Games include 'Word Search,' which calls for finding hidden words in a grid of letters and 'Flash Card,' which flashes a word that kids then have to reproduce. Kids move on to spelling bees in hopes of competing at the (animated) White House. A big plus is that customized word lists can be added, making this a useful homework tool. It disappoints only with its multimedia: "video-game like graphics" don't meet today's standards.

SUPER STREET FIGHTER II
18 18 18 **16**

$$$

GameTek, Inc.
DOS

Games/Combat

This classic 2-D fighting game brings "all of the action... and fun of the arcade" game to the PC. Less gruesome than *Mortal Kombat*, this is like a brawl between Popeye and Bluto—cartoon fighters pound each other until one sees stars. The trick is in learning the moves. Only down and dirty street smarts unleash the combatants hurricane kicks. But it's "horribly dated," making it "too far behind the curve to appeal to cutting edge gamers."

SYNNERGIST

— — —

$$$
21st Century Entertainment, Inc.   DOS
Games/Role Playing & Interactive Fiction

With a string of successful pinball games under their belts, 21st Century Entertainment takes a stab at its first graphic adventure game in this two-disc set. Set in dystopic New Arhus in year 2010 (sound familiar?), *Synnergist* allows players to take the role of Tim Machin, a reporter trying to track down the nasty who killed his friend. Machin can talk to anyone in the city, and the mystery has a number of possible outcomes.

SYSTEM SHOCK

19 21 22 **21**

$$$
Origin Systems, Inc.   DOS
Games/Combat

So you think *Doom* is cool? Watch out, 'cause first-person perspective games have gone big-time with System Shock, a mind-blowing experience unlike anything else on the shelves. "One of the most completely immersive games out," you've got only your wits to help you accumulate massive firepower to bring down mutants, robots and, finally, the evil Shodan. This is a "real memory hog"— a huge game with remarkable graphics and sound.

TAKE YOUR BEST SHOT

17 16 16 **17**

$
7th Level   Win
Games/Arcade

An interactive cartoon slug-fest packed with lots of fun extras. Bill Plympton's animated businessmen provide the characters (and victims) for this set of three "hilarious" games—knockoffs of the old Pong, Breakout and baseball. Extras include icons, screen savers, Windows wallpaper and audio clips. The disc is "great fun," but some might find the "violent" material offensive, and at about $20, these basic games can "get old fast."

TANK COMMANDER

13 11 11 **12**

$$$
Domark Software, Inc.   DOS
Games/Combat

As *TC*, you'd better start worrying—your gunner's "accuracy is lousy." Sometimes he's right on, other times he can't hit the side of a barn. This inconsistency isn't your only problem—shells go through solid objects, distant images wink on and off. Unique features like zoomable satellites and helicopter cams are neat, but they don't function in network or modem play. "Poorly designed and badly executed," this campaign misses the mark.

TAXI

$$$

News Electronic Data, Inc.   Win/Mac
Travel

Feel like a native at your next destination! *Taxi* indexes thousands of hotels and restaurants and gives the inside scoop with Zagat Surveys ratings. It's also a mapping tool, though graphics are rudimentary, which locates desired stops and prints out ideal routes. Helpful control icon descriptors make it easy to use. Not designed for vacation travel (it doesn't list sights), *Taxi* is an "excellent planning tool for business travelers" and residents of the represented metropolitan areas. There are several versions, each covering five major cities. For road warriors, a 20-city version is available for about $160.

TFX: TACTICAL FIGHTER EXPERIMENT

– – – 14
$

Ocean Software Ltd.   DOS
Games/Combat

You might not have served in the Persian Gulf War, but this program is about as close as it gets. Although it features some of the most advanced plane designs, this two-year-old flight simulator shows its age: the graphics are grainy and the text is often hard to read. Nevertheless, *TFX* has an impressive scope of weapons, interaction and missions. Fun for enthusiasts, but it leaves casual gamers breathing fumes.

THINKIN' THINGS, COLLECTION 1

21 21 20 20
Ages: 4-8 $$

Edmark Corporation   Win/Mac/DOS
Kids/Edugames-General

Memory and problem-solving skills are given a "unique" workout in this "great kids' program." Each activity can be engaged with in multiple ways, allowing for a variety of learning styles. In Oranga Banga, for example, kids choose either a memory game with rhythms, or creative play and recording of percussion sounds. Parents give it top ratings for "logic" and "problem solving," and though some say it needs more "zing," it's a "favorite" among kids.

THINKIN' THINGS, COLLECTION 2

21 22 23 22
Ages: 6-12 $$

Edmark Corporation   Win/Mac/DOS
Kids/Edugames-General

"Continuing the explorability" of *Collection I*, these somewhat more advanced activities employ the same successful approach to critical thinking. Activities include creating artistic, moving patterns, scripting out music, a concentration game with tones, and drawing one-dimensional designs onto spinning 3-D shapes. Some say this title encourages creative thinking and artistic experimentation "like no other program."

THIS IS SPINAL TAP

20 20 21 **20**
$

Voyager Company Win/Mac
Movies

Crank up the volume, and rock out, man. Fans who "love the movie will love this disc." The CD has the entire 82-minute movie on it, plus some handy "full-search" features and a "nice interface." The video is a bit grainy but the sound is good quality, and the controls resemble an on-screen VCR. It's funny and behind-the-scenes, and fans of the movie find this title lets them tap in a little further.

TIME ALMANAC 1995

– – – **19**
$$$

Softkey International Win/Mac
Current Affairs

The pages of Time unfold with multimedia majesty in this well-designed almanac. Every word of every issue from 1989 to January, 1995 is here. These are supplemented with a collection of Time articles on people and events of the 20th century, special reports on major issues, statistics, charts and maps of the U.S. and a news trivia game. Articles connect to over 60 videos and 1000 photos, slides, charts and covers. There's a lot here.

TIME ALMANAC OF THE 20TH CENTURY

19 18 20 **19**
$$

Compact Publishing, Inc. Win
History

Time articles are accompanied by video and audio for a multimedia perusal of the people and events of the century thus far. A pleasingly simple interface makes this CD of "great reference material" extremely easy to use. A quiz game allows you to assume the role of a Time editor with a 5:00 o'clock deadline. Parents and grandparents can use this CD to share the events that shaped their lives with the younger generation.

TOM JACKSON PRESENTS THE PERFECT RESUME

16 12 13 **16**

See *Perfect Resume*.

TONY LARUSSA BASEBALL 3

21 19 19 **19**
$$

Stormfront Studios DOS
Games/Sports Simulation

With smooth 256-color high resolution graphics, richly detailed 3-D stadiums, and a myriad of special features, this "canny, satisfying upgrade" is a computer baseball marvel. Throw in the voice of Hall of Fame broadcaster Mel Allen, and it's easy to ignore the occasional "mediocre game performance," like animation glitches (too many singles off the right field wall). This game covers all the bases with drafting, player creation, fantasy general manager, and lightning fast automatic replay.

TORIN'S PASSAGE

- - -

$$$

Sierra On-Line, Inc. Win

Games/Role Playing & Interactive Fiction

Can the creator of the *Leisure Suit Larry* series turn over a new leaf and trade raunchy humor for family fare? Since Al Lowe wrote this one for his 11-year-old daughter, we certainly hope so. Players help Torin, a young man, search for his parents who have been trapped by a magic spell in the world of Strata. Disney-like animation and music by Academy Award-winning composer Michel Legrand (*Yentl*) promise to make this attractive for all ages.

TORTOISE AND THE HARE

22 23 23 **23**

Ages: 3-8 $$

Living Books Win/Mac

Kids/Stories

If Aesop knew his classic story of patience and perseverance would one day make it to a CD-ROM, he might turn over in his grave. Once he had a chance to play with it, however, it might be hard to tear him away. "Kids love this program," and the producers hold true to the original storyline. As with all the Living Books, there are plenty of highlighted words and clickable objects with "incredible" sound and graphics.

TRANSPARENT LANGUAGE NOW! SERIES

Transparent Language Win/Mac

Language

This "simple" series stands apart with a no-frills, slightly "boring" but "pretty effective" approach. At the heart of each program is a dialogue box containing a native language article, essay or short story. This is supplemented with audio boxes for pronunciation, and translation boxes that translate words and phrases. It's "a pleasant way to learn to read" another language, and users find it "really works." If you don't need a "sexier interface," the *Now!* series gets the job done. The newer, unevaluated version, adds some graphics and a voice recording feature. Individual titles are listed under *French Now!*, *German Now!*, etc.

TRANSPORT TYCOON

18 19 19 **19**

$$

MicroProse Software, Inc. DOS

Games/Simulation

SimCity 2000 lovers, take heed! Grab your money bags, use them to build railroads, airlines, roads and shipping lines, and little towns will start popping up all along your route. The only goal is to increase your wealth—and if you don't do it, your rivals will. Try not to get lost in the greed or the levels of gorgeous graphics that can eventually befuddle players. There are "endless hours of gameplay" here. A new, pricier deluxe version includes modem play and pre-saved scenarios.

TRAVELRAMA USA

Ages: 8 & up $

Sanctuary Woods Multimedia Corporation Win/Mac

Kids/Edugames-Social Studies

In this interactive cross-country geography game, players search for popular American tourist sites and collect postcards while budgeting mileage and earning bonus airplane tickets. *Travelrama* is full of personality, with attractive and engaging artwork. However, there's little information on each state, so player strategies get reduced to random guessing. In short, it's an electronic version of Go Fish, making it most appropriate for the young folk.

TREASURE COVE!

Ages: 5-9 $$

The Learning Company Win/Mac

Kids/Edugames-General

The Master of Mischief is polluting Treasure Cove with Goobies. Kids swim through the sea firing their airgun at starfish. By hitting the right ones, they get multiple-choice questions to solve. Correct answers help find gems to repair a bridge and plug up holes to prevent Goobies from getting into the cove. It's "fun" but parent's find it dated, and the poor quality graphics aren't in league with the rest of the *Treasure* series.

TREASURE GALAXY!

Ages: 5-9 $$

The Learning Company Win/Mac

Kids/Edugames-Math

In "perhaps the best" of the *Treasure* series, kids search for missing crystals while whizzing along in space scooters. Along the way they capture "sundrops" that activate math games on measurement, calendar dates, number patterns and basic fractions. Educationally sound games use reward, in the form of "star bucks," to keep kids moving toward other games and harder levels. This is a "fun" fantasy/arcade game that uses a point system to motivate kids.

TREASURE MATHSTORM!

Ages: 5-9 $$

The Learning Company Win/Mac

Kids/Edugames-Math

By capturing elves and answering their math questions correctly, kids gather and return the castle-on-the-mountain treasure that has been scattered by a snowstorm. This fun program holds kids' attention "for hours" and, with six difficulty levels, keeps them coming back "for months." Well done time-telling and money-counting games add real world value. Math facts stick to addition and subtraction. "Excellent" for kids who like videogames and reward-oriented learning.

TREASURE MOUNTAIN!

20 20 18 **18**

Ages: 6-8 $$

The Learning Company   Win/Mac
Kids/Edugames-Math
Kids climb a mountain searching for treasure and learn "on the side." By piecing together clues, they find the gold key that leads to the next level in this arcade style game. Ultimately, kids fight the "Master of Mischief" by answering math story problems. Not the most advanced graphics, but an excellent game that kids "love". Like all the Treasure titles, it's an "enjoyable" reward based game.

TRIPLEPLAY PLUS! ENGLISH

19 18 15 **18**

Syracuse Language Systems   Win
Language/English
Triple Play teaches 1000 word and phrases "by immersion," meaning no English is used, with games that get more complicated as you gain proficiency. Students choose games from three levels (level 1 teaches nouns, verbs, and phrases, level 2 moves on to sentences, and level 3 includes dialogue and colloquial expressions), then three modes—aural comprehension, reading, or speaking—and finally, six subjects, like food or people and clothing. It's a non-linear approach that leaves some beginners floundering in frustration. But this "fun and educational" series has its highlights: the well done voice recognition lets you have a "conversation with the computer." It's even picky about pronunciation!

TRIPLEPLAY PLUS! FRENCH

20 16 14 **17**

Syracuse Language Systems   Win
Language/French
See *TriplePlay Plus! English.*

TRIPLEPLAY PLUS! GERMAN

– – – **18**

Syracuse Language Systems   Win
Language/German
See *TriplePlay Plus! English.*

TRIPLEPLAY PLUS! SPANISH

20 20 19 **19**

Syracuse Language Systems   Win
Language/Spanish
See *TriplePlay Plus! English*

C M U O

TRIVIAL PURSUIT
13 18 13 **13**

$$$

Virgin Interactive Entertainment   Win/Mac
Games/Parlor

Fans of the board game expecting something better should forget it. "This is a big disappointment," especially if you've spotted "Interactive" in the box title. The "interactivity" consists of saying your answer out loud, asking the computer for the right answer, and seeing if it matches. There are lots of animations, but many don't relate to the question. Stick to the original; you don't need to call tech support to get that one to run.

TROGGLE TROUBLE MATH
15 18 15 **16**

Ages: 6-12 $$$

MECC   Win/Mac
Kids/Edugames-Math

It's a busy time helping Sparky, the math dog, rescue the Muncher from Dr. Frankentroggle. There's storing bones to pay for activities, warding off Troggles by solving math problems, keeping up energy with math calculations, and gathering clues. Phew! It "vies for the hearts of Treasure fans,"…the trouble is, there aren't "very many" math problems so it "doesn't keep you interested," and the difficult arcade action makes completing the ultimate mission "an almost impossible goal."

TROUBLE IS MY BUSINESS
14 14 12 **13**

$$$

Time-Warner Interactive Group   Win
Literature

Fictional P.I. Philip Marlowe is the original 1940's "boozy, jaded gumshoe" so often parodied. This disc brings that "smoke and sleaze ambiance" to life through the text of the Marlowe library, narration, photos and letters written by Chandler. The movies are scant and only tangentially related to the novels. If you've never experienced Chandler before, you'll find it "gripping," though tiresome to read from the screen. "Chandler fans will love it."

TUNELAND
20 21 21 **20**

Ages: 3 & up $$

7th Level   Win
Kids/Music

This title "keeps grandkids entertained for hours!!" Combining cute graphics and fluid animation *TuneLand* stays interesting screen after screen. Each graphic is loaded with clickable objects and characters—many producing songs. It's "easy to use," with "great" sounds and graphics. Howie Mandel's sense of humor shows through on such choice classics as the reggae version of 'This Little Piggy' and the wonderful jazz arrangement of 'Hush Now Baby.'

TWAIN'S WORLD

Bureau of Electronic Publishing
Literature

Users are "less than impressed" with the quantity and quality of illustrations and animations in this title. And the "unintuitive" interface means it can take a little while to figure out. But with almost all Twain's written work, it shines as a "research tool." You can search Twain's novels, stories, essays, letters and speeches for references to specific words and phrases, making this a "treasure trove" for Twain scholars.

U.S. NAVY FIGHTERS

Electronic Arts
Games/Combat

Real Navy fighters need lots of power; this flight simulation is no exception. The box says 486/25, but that's only if you want to jerk and sputter your way through the clouds. A top-of-the-line Pentium, however, will give you "some of the best photo-realistic graphics and resolution" around. Choose from 50 "realistic missions," design your own, or go whole hog and do an extended tour of duty. With the right horsepower, it's take-off!

ULTIMATE DOMAIN

Mindscape
Games/Simulation

Hate making decisions? Do yourself a favor and stay away from this builder/simulation which is so "packed with details," you'll be twitching in minutes. However, if you consider yourself a master strategist, then take on the challenge of creating and maintaining a medieval empire. Unlike similar games, your turns are timed, and so you frequently find yourself "rushing about from task to task," hoping to beat the clock before your village is demolished.

ULTIMATE DOOM

GT Interactive Software
Games/Combat

You always suspected there were more *Doom* levels hidden away in a vault somewhere, didn't you? Well, here they are—eight new ones plus a secret level if you can find it—together with the original three-part Doom game. No, these aren't knockoffs that some teenager hacked together; these come straight from the original maker, Id Software. And they are tougher, with graphics that are distinctively different from the rest. A *Doom*-ers dream come true.

ULTIMATE FOOTBALL '95

‒ ‒ ‒ 21
$$$

MicroProse Software, Inc. DOS
Games/Sports Simulation
Using an accurate physical model of football, this title takes you into the trenches in an amazing real-time simulation. Review the action with topnotch instant replay, and marvel at the individual moves of every player. Play calling is confusing, but spectacular 3-D graphics and camera angles make the learning curve worth it. Franchise Football League software is also included, complete with fantasy football design and management options.

ULTIMATE FRANK LLOYD WRIGHT: AMERICA'S ARCHITECT

18 16 18 18
$$

Microsoft Corporation Win/Mac
Art Appreciation
The man and his art are both introduced in this "extensive" biographical reference. This title's interface may be "a bit dark," but Wright's genius shines through in images of his designs. Users are privy to information about Wright…as an architect, designer, and also as "the philosopher and person." An illustrated chronology of major buildings and excerpts from Wright's writings help put his oeuvre in perspective.

ULTIMATE HAUNTED HOUSE

17 20 17 19

See *Gahan Wilson's The Ultimate Haunted House.*

ULTIMATE HUMAN BODY

21 20 21 20
$$$

Dorling Kindersley Publishing, Inc. Win/Mac
Science/Anatomy
This "very informative" basic presentation of gross and microscopic anatomy has 700 linked screens with information on the body and its processes. It answers such parent-stoppers as: 'Why do we yawn?' and 'Why does the eye produce tears?' The sound effects are clever, the 5-second animations "ingenious," the interface "nice," and the search function allows you to navigate lots of information.

UNDER A KILLING MOON

21 24 19 22
$$$$

Access Software, Inc. DOS
Games/Mystery
This four-disc set was an early entrant in the interactive movie genre. With a dollop of Dashiel Hammett attitude and deadpan humor a la Columbo, this "very smooth" title puts the user in control of a gritty detective story. The graphics—particularly the animation—are "extraordinary," though the controls "leave something to be desired." Users find the plot "witty," "challenging," "addictive," and "beautiful;" lamenting they don't have "enough time to play."

UNDERSEA ADVENTURE

– – – 18

Ages: 5-12 $$

Knowledge Adventure   Win/DOS
Kids/Edugames-Science

The content, best suited to kids under 10, covers favorite underwater creatures—including sharks, dolphins, whales and tropical fish. For diversion there are some quizzes, preschool storybooks, and the 'Marine Animal Lab,' where kids examine the parts of three creatures. The '3-D Undersea World' is less successful; it's "awkward" to explore and doesn't give kids "much to do." But "top quality" photos and "solid information" give kids a "nice overview of marine studies."

UNDERSTANDING BREAST CANCER

– – – 12

$$$

ISM, Inc.   Win
Medical Reference

Soothing pictures of sandy beaches hover behind lines of text. Soft voices calmly discuss prevention and surgery techniques. This dignified package aims to help women understand breast cancer. A "potentially great idea," but the interface is "annoying and clumsy" and the information is "only slightly more-in-depth than an American Cancer Society brochure." Despite some well presented sections, like one explaining radiation therapy, this title falls short.

UNDERSTANDING EXPOSURE

19 13 22 17

$$

DiAMAR Interactive Corporation   Win/Mac
Photography

Say c-h-e-e-e-s-e! The skill of photography goes well beyond point and shoot disposables and this "very good program" out-shoots competitors with careful focus on all aspects of the art. The user gets detailed lessons on film speed, shutter speed, depth of field and much more, and comes away with a basic understanding of photographic principles. The exquisite pictures that accompany the text make this title "enjoyable" as well as educational.

UNNECESSARY ROUGHNESS '95

16 19 15 15

$$

Accolade, Inc.   DOS
Games/Sports Simulation

Armchair quarterbacks with fast PCs will find this a good but not great simulation. There's plenty to do—start an exhibition game or fight to get to the Super Bowl. The action can be watched from lots of angles, including a "helmet cam," while Al Michaels calls the play-by-plays. But the game controls are "sluggish" and the action is "choppy" without a zippy PC, unless you shut off the sound and settle for silent football. Now that's an experience.

C M U O

UNNECESSARY ROUGHNESS '96

– – –

$$$

Accolade, Inc.   DOS
Games/Sports Simulation

This pro football simulation is gathering steam and over-taking its predecessor, with improved artificial intelligence, over 1000 NFL style plays, custom play design, and over 125 league leader stats. Other additions include a detailed box score, general manager with salary cap function, and four new player attributes (for a total of nine). There's also added animations for smoother running, tackles and pass plays, and Al Michaels returns to the broadcast booth for the play-by-play.

VIETNAM

21 22 21 **21**

$$

Medio Multimedia Inc.   Win
History/War

Two decades after the fall of Saigon, this "fascinating" title beckons you with the facts, emotions, anger, conflict, personalities, controversy and loss of the "enormous tragedy" of the Vietnam War. A "moving" collection of "clear" video footage, Pulitzer-prize-winning photos and history, combine to make this a unique historical and educational perspective on a devastating war. A captivating, first-rate multimedia documentary.

VIRTUAL GUITAR: WELCOME TO WEST FEEDBACK

– – – **21**

$$$

Ahead   Win
Games/Role Playing & Interactive Fiction

An air guitarist's dream come true, requiring no musical skill beyond keeping time. The 'Guitar' consists of a large, plastic electronic pick which plugs into your computer and, after some tweaking, works just fine on your tennis racket. Following a chart that looks like an EKG from the doctor, you strum along to rock tunes, starting in an adolescent's bedroom, and, if you're good, ending onstage in a stadium with Aerosmith. Great graphics in this rock 'n' roll dream.

VIRTUAL POOL

20 23 21 **21**

$$

Interplay Productions   DOS
Games/Parlor

This terrific simulation solves the dilemma of not having enough space or cash to install a private billiards table. Choose from 9-ball, 8-ball, rotation, and straight pool, and then take a virtual stroll around the table to size up your shots. Play a friend, the PC, or even someone long-distance via modem. Videos recall the history of pool, give advice on your game, and show trick shots. "All the ambiance of a pool hall, without the smoke."

VIRTUAL VEGAS VOLUME ONE BLACKJACK

- - - 15
$

Virtual Vegas   Win/Mac
Games/Parlor

If scantily-clad women dealing cards and insults in a plush casino setting is your cup of tea, this is the title for you. Although the dialogue, written by editors of *National Lampoon*, can be somewhat "ridiculous," the title boasts good graphics and lots of so-called interaction, as dealers "pepper you with zingers." The program claims true voice recognition technology, but like batteries in kids toys, the required software and microphone not included.

VORTEX: QUANTUM GATE II

13 17 13 12
$$$

HyperBole Studios   Win/Mac
Games/Role Playing & Interactive Fiction

A continuation of *Quantum Gate: The Saga Begins*, this "disorienting" mix of film and game has players take the protagonist, Griffin, through his encounters with humans and aliens as he seeks the truth about the Aylinde, giant insect-like creatures, and why humans are invading their planet. Players select from lists of questions and statements to direct Griffins actions. It's a "bizarre" trip with "decent" acting, but a somewhat preachy script. Installation can be a "nightmare."

VOYEUR

14 17 14 16
Ages: 17 & up $$$

Interplay Productions   Mac/DOS
Games/Mystery

Be a voyeur in this "trashy" interactive drama. From across the street, train your camera on the home of a corrupt presidential candidate, played by I-Spy's Robert Culp, who is plotting to kill one of the skeletons in his closet. By watching, and taping the right scenes, you can stop him. But "the clock is running" and things change each time you play. The "moody" soundtrack and "(almost) torrid" sex scenes are "entertaining," but after a while it gets "tedious."

WARCRAFT: ORCS AND HUMANS

20 21 22 22
$$$

Blizzard Entertainment   Mac/DOS
Games/Role Playing & Interactive Fiction

Tired of being a human? Always wanted to be a fiendish Orc? This real-time, tactical combat game gives you the opportunity to take either side—and then try to conquer the Kingdom of Azeroth. "It's good when you play against the computer, great when two people compete on a modem." Once you get the hang of the controls, "the whole family will love it." It's the kind of "game that makes one late for work."

WARPLANES: MODERN FLYING AIRCRAFT

18 17 15 **18**
$$$

Maris Multimedia — Win/Mac
Science/General

Top-gun wannabees or CIA analysts now have a tool tailor made for them. *Warplanes* takes you inside the ultimate modern fighting machine—providing "loving, almost obsessive" details about everything from electronics equipment listings to weapons specs. Although the three included flight simulators aren't "full-featured," they're still "fun," and the "powerful" audio and "elegant" interface help make this package a "definitive" guide to military aviation.

WARREN MILLER'S SKI WORLD

19 18 19 **20**
Ages: 12 & up $$

Multicom Publishing, Inc. — Win/Mac
Sports Reference

This 'hot dog' styled disc is the perfect mid-summer distraction for die-hards dreaming about their first run of the season. It's a joy to glide through, with a "handsome Windows interface," "an intriguing combination of material," instructional video tips for all levels and a history of the sport. The resort index offers details on new destinations, with video, ratings and trail maps. Look up your favorite ski star in the record book. Tailor-made for ski enthusiasts.

WAY THINGS WORK

22 21 21 **22**
Ages: 8 & up $$$

Dorling Kindersley Publishing, Inc. — Win/Mac
Kids/Science

"If you liked the book, you'll love this CD," covering 200+ inventions under the categories Machines, Principles of Science and History and Inventors. "Beautiful" illustrations prompt wonderful animations that detail the inner workings of things, their design and function. There's lots here, even a timeline, and it's all very accessible. But difficult stuff gets light treatment—it's "not a quick fix for the technologically impaired." Multi-leveled information "provides hours of fun" for the technically curious of all ages.

WEBSTER'S INTERACTIVE ENCYCLOPEDIA

11 15 11 **10**
Ages: 11 & up $$

Attica Cybernetics Ltd. — Win
Reference/Encyclopedias

Considering the plethora of similar programs, this one earns pretty low marks all around. Boasting 34,000 articles, 30 minutes of video, 150 audio clips and 3,500 illustrations, this title should have been a contender. Alas, the interaction is "slow" and "mediocre," and the content is "uneven." Competing programs feature more video, audio and user-friendlier interfaces. If you see *Webster's* in the bargain bin, pick it up. Otherwise, leave it for the uninformed. *This disc is available, under a slightly different name, in the 5 ft. 10 pak Collector's edition.*

WEEKEND HOME PROJECTS

20 21 19 **20**

See *Hometime Weekend Home Projects.*

WELCOME TO BODYLAND

12 14 13 **11**

Ages: 5-11 $

IVI, Inc. Win/Mac

Science/Anatomy

A theme park with 13 body part attractions? Unfortunately "pleasing graphics" and "toe tapping musical themes" are not enough to save this title. Though its mission is to "answer all the right questions," it disappoints with extremely limited interactivity and explanations that "lack clarity." There's not enough for younger kids to do and not enough information to satisfy older users. This is a case where a "book could do a better job for lots less money."

WESTERN GARDEN

20 15 22 **17**

$$$

Sunset New Media Win/Mac

House and Garden

Seasoned gardeners and neophytes will enjoy using this disc to plan the ultimate Western garden. The simple interface allows you to cross-reference climate, nutrition requirements and plant types to determine the ideal plant for that problem spot in your yard. Twenty-nine videos show the experts in action. Sunset has "turned a famous reference book into an even better CD-ROM."

WHAT'S THE SECRET?

20 19 19 **19**

Ages: 8-12 $$

3M Learning Software Win/Mac

Kids/Edugames-Science

This "nice title" proves all scientific discovery starts with curiosity. With copious video, animation and sound effects, this nonlinear exploration draws users in with questions like 'Why do bears hibernate?' and 'What's in blood?' "Good activities," a "wide range of material" and interactive experiments, make learning science a child's game. Forty-five hidden 'patches' to uncover and collect help keep users motivated. Billed for all ages, the youthful tone makes it best for kids.

WHEEL OF FORTUNE

18 10 12 **15**

$$

Sony ImageSoft Win

Games/Parlor

Wh-eeee-l ooof Foooortuuuune! Pat Sajak isn't around but the lovely Vanna is here for your viewing pleasure. Otherwise, this "occasionally amusing" game looks just like TV. While these puzzles can be quite "challenging," it's not all razzle dazzle. The "simple" interface is too "slow," and the "limited" videos are "repetitive" and "get tiring to watch." And there's one major, unfixable flaw—no lovely parting gifts when you lose.

WHERE IN THE USA IS CARMEN SANDIEGO?

21 21 22 **21**

Ages: 9 & up $$$

Broderbund Software, Inc. Win/Mac
Kids/Edugames-Social Studies

Young detectives track Carmen and her criminal cohorts through the U.S., focusing on American geography, topography, culture and landmarks en route. Accessing the topographic maps and state photos is easy, though some generic photos seem unrelated to any particular state. Creative controls (like a Videophone to communicate with headquarters) and provocative clues add to the fun—kids learn without realizing it. It's also entertaining to use "as a family."

WHERE IN THE WORLD IS CARMEN SANDIEGO?

21 21 22 **22**

Ages: 9 & up $$$

Broderbund Software, Inc. Win/Mac
Kids/Edugames-Social Studies

Search the world for criminals in this "jazzier" version of a now classic edugame. Learn about geography and cultures as you collect evidence. "Stunning" visuals and great music genuinely increase awareness of what places are like. Some complain that the judge's comments get "repetitive" and that the travel agent "gets boring," but overall it's an "excellent," "classy" game and a "great geography lesson" for kids "who like a little mystery with their education." Good reading skills a requisite.

WHERE IN THE WORLD IS CARMEN SANDIEGO? JUNIOR DETECTIVE EDITION

20 22 21 **20**

Ages: 5-8 $$

Broderbund Software, Inc. Win/Mac
Kids/Edugames-Social Studies

Younger kids can learn about geography while searching for criminals in this version of the venerable Carmen Sandiego. Clues are visual rather than written and a character provides verbal help, making this game accessible to non-readers. Some say its "surprisingly short lived" while others think it's "lasting fun" and "humorous, engaging, educationally sound." All feel it gives children "an excellent introduction to geography." Youngsters "love" this "exceptional...all around great" game.

WHERE'S WALDO? AT THE CIRCUS

– – – **19**

Ages: 4-9 $$

WarnerActive Win/Mac
Kids/Edugames-Math

Waldo's here, if you can find him, in "colorful, dynamic style" that's "true to the spirit of the book." Kids search for Waldo in randomly variable locations and play games in four circus environments. Along the way, clicking on the right spots brings up lots of amusing animations. The clever, multi-leveled games have kids doing things like organizing band players by pitch or feeding lions the right number of treats. It's fun, but could be more intuitive— kids need help getting started.

WHO BUILT AMERICA?

$$

Voyager Company
Mac
History
Based on a "left-leaning" textbook on U.S. social history from 1876 to 1914, this title "goes far beyond the book" to include extra historical documents, photos, charts, audio clips and video clips from early movies. Covering a period of industrialization, immigration and labor unrest, this history focuses on ordinary people. With "well written text" and "carefully chosen" supplemental material, it's "more of a text book than light reading," probably best for schools and libraries.

WHO KILLED BRETT PENANCE?

— — — 17
$

Creative Multimedia Corporation
Win/Mac
Games/Mystery
Based on the concept that most crimes are solved within six hours, that's the amount of game time you have to figure out who killed Brett Penance, Elspeth Haskard, Sam Rupert, or Taylor French. With access to the crime scene, forensic and witness reports, suspect interviews, and expert testimony, these adult whodunnits challenge your analytical skills. Once you've determined the culprit, pushy reporters grill you to see if you're right. *Sam Rupert* is the first and "weakest" of the series since it offers only one solution to the crime. The others have three different endings for increased game life. *Brett Penance* and *Taylor French* feature actress Sheryl Lee (aka Laura Palmer of Twin Peaks) as your assistant detective. An "interesting and unique approach" to interactive mystery gaming. Look for money-saving series bundle Christmas 1995.

WHO KILLED ELSBETH HASKARD? (THE MAGIC DEATH)

— — — 17
$

Creative Multimedia Corporation
Win
Games/Mystery
See *Who Killed Brett Penance?*.

WHO KILLED SAM RUPERT?

— — — 12
$

Creative Multimedia Corporation
Win/Mac
Games/Mystery
See *Who Killed Brett Penance?*.

WHO KILLED TAYLOR FRENCH?

17 20 17 16
$

Creative Multimedia Corporation
Win/Mac
Games/Mystery
See *Who Killed Brett Penance?*.

		C	M	U	O

WHY DO WE HAVE TO?

16 15 12 13

Ages: 2-7 $

StarPress Multimedia   Win/Mac
Kids/Edugames-General

A cute interactive story that conveys the importance of having and following rules. It's filled out with a few solid, if unimaginative, activities, including the requisite matching game. The graphics and animation are not up there with the best of breed, but kids like the story and if you want your 2- to 5-year-old to get the message it delivers, this is a palatable way for them to receive it.

WIDGET WORKSHOP

18 23 21 18

Ages: 8 & up $$

Maxis   Win/Mac
Kids/Science

Configure your own weird widgets with a variety of building elements from cats to light bulbs—complete with appropriate sound effects. Get your inspiration from the many puzzles available to solve, some of which elucidate scientific phenomena. While adults may "spend thirty minutes using it and have no idea what they're doing," "kids love it!" Widget is fun for inventive minds starved for wacky brain-bending challenges!

WIGGINS IN STORYLAND

18 20 16 17

Ages: 4-7 $$

Virgin Sound & Vision   Win
Kids/Art & Writing

This story-writing disc with a fantasy twist includes a "rich," humorous and "wonderfully educational" activity area where children hear great literary excerpts by the likes of Twain and Poe. The "easy and fun to use" storymaker lets budding raconteurs choose among eight themes, such as fairy tales or monsters. Just don't expect realism—no true-to-life characters or settings are here. A wonderful tool for fantasy lovers; stories can be narrated, animated, and background music added.

WIGGLEWORKS

21 20 19 21

Ages: 3-6 $$

Apple Computer, Inc.   Mac
Kids/Art & Writing

A story writer that includes 3 "irresistible" tales, "geared toward beginning readers," that kids can listen to, read alone and alter to their hearts' content. "Fun" writing, drawing and painting tools encourage original story creations. Kids can narrate their own work or let Wiggle-Works read them. But beginning writers need outside feedback and encouragement or they "grow bored" so, while it's a very good program, it will "probably find more use at school" than at home.

WILD BLUE YONDER, EPISODE 1: 50 YEARS OF GS AND JETS

18 18 19 **18**
$$

Spectrum Holobyte, Inc.   Win/Mac
Science/General

Modern Warplanes. There's a subject many might find "boring." If you don't, (and maybe if you do)—this "expertly crafted" disc is for you. Produced from footage shot for an Emmy-award winning documentary, it features 20 planes, from WWII to futuristic machines still in development. it's a "wealth of information"—war stories, specs such as top speeds, weapons and short video clips. The graphics and interface "give multimedia a good name."

WILD CARDS

13 15 15 **13**
$

Corel Corporation   Win/Mac
Games/Parlor

Okay, parents hate this. The zippy animated "Roger Rabbit nightmare" cast is straight from Saturday Morning Cartoon Hell. But kids at least tolerate it. With seven well-explained games including War, Crazy Eights Hearts, 21 and Fish, the in-your-face graphics are "obnoxious" and "zany," and sporadic crashes kill some games. *Wild Cards* actually teaches skills other than card-sharking—strategy, matching, memory—but unless opponents aren't around, kids probably will prefer a "real deck."

WINE GUIDE

24 20 23 **24**
$$

Microsoft Corporation   Win/Mac
Wine, Beer & Spirits

This CD's functionality is "astounding," a "veritable cornucopia" of wine lore. Author Oz Clarke, praised for his "charming enthusiasm" for wine, guides you with many "short but helpful" videos. Highlights from the dozens of sections include a Wine Atlas with regional vintage reports, and a "wonderful" facility that lets you match nearly 6000 wines against numerous criteria, including price, grape type and suitable food. Knock 'em dead at the next wine tasting.

WINES OF THE WORLD

18 15 17 **16**
$$

Multicom Publishing, Inc.   Win/Mac
Wine, Beer & Spirits

How is a Burgundy made? Who are the different producers? What do the labels look like? If you have ever wondered about these things, then this "elegant" CD-ROM will definitely interest you. Vintage, rating, price, quality and dozens of other interesting facts about thousands of wines are included. Although it might be "a little redundant for the expert," this title will satisfy most casual wine enthusiasts.

WING COMMANDER III: HEART OF THE TIGER

23 25 24 **24**
$$$
DOS

Origin Systems, Inc.
Games/Combat

It's generally considered a winner: "5½ out of 5 stars" and "can't say enough about it." Appreciated for its playability and cinematic graphics, stars Mark Hamill and Malcolm McDowell deliver movie-quality performances. Many find it "an excellent mix of sight and sound," "just as much fun to watch as to play." But be warned: this memory-hungry program needs top-of-the-line PCs—owners of lesser machines say "installation is pure hell"

WINGS OF GLORY

18 20 17 **19**
$$$
DOS

Origin Systems, Inc.
Games/Combat

German flying ace Gertmann is on your tail and all that's keeping you above the French countryside is your WWI bi-plane that looks like it was put together with spit and glue. If you survive, there are 44 more missions to fly with four other planes. This unusual simulation sports "impressive graphics" and "interesting camera angles." While "hitting your targets is frustrating," in 1917 just staying airborne was a feat. "Red Baron with better graphics."

WINGS OVER EUROPE

20 18 15 **18**
$$
Win/Mac

Discovery Home Entertainment
History/War

The Discovery Channel brings its wares to multimedia with this documentary-style CD-ROM. This title provides "lots of information" about eight warplanes that played crucial roles in the European theater during WWII. Each episode describes planes, battles, missions and flying aces through video, "good graphics" and text. A warning however: if you are not overwhelmed with curiosity about the air war over Europe, this title may be "too much propaganda" for you.

WINNIE THE POOH AND THE HONEY TREE

- - - **19**
Ages: 3-7 $$
Win/Mac

Disney Interactive
Kids/Stories

Disney's cartoon Pooh-bear makes a graceful transition to CD-ROM. This narrated storybook highlights words and has clickable animations. Two more original features are a music icon that brings up sing-along songs and a book icon that highlights words that kids can click for in-context definitions. Narrations and animations, while good, are also uninterruptible, limiting the flexibility of an otherwise nice storybook.

WOLF

17 16 14 **16**

$$

Sanctuary Woods Multimedia Corporation   Win/DOS
Games/Simulation

This game-like educational title takes "simulation" to a new level of realism. The user literally becomes the wolf, forced to do everything a Canis Lupus must in order to survive: hunt, mate, and protect its young. In the wilds of the office, "it has held the interest of more than one of my co-workers." Perhaps leery at first, some users wind up enjoying this title quite a bit.

WORD ATTACK 3

21 15 19 **20**

Ages: 10 & up $$

Davidson & Associates, Inc.   Mac/DOS
Kids/Edugames-Reading

An upgrade to Word Attack Plus, this vocabulary builder covers spelling bee attacks too. Activities are built around chosen words, picked from the 3200 words included or custom added. A presentation area provides definitions and uses words in context. Then kids go to activities such as a maze game where they choose correct definitions to keep moving. User-chosen lists mean this is a "great way to study for a vocabulary test," and kids "don't get bored."

WORD CITY

- - - **18**

Ages: 7-14 $$

Sanctuary Woods Multimedia Corporation   Win/Mac
Kids/Edugames-Reading

Fun word games in an arcade setting bait kids into saving Word City from "Snorkelers." Games involve such skills as spelling, definitions, reading comprehension, and picking from a group of letters to make a list of words. Users say it has "an engaging format" with "lots of challenging levels" and good game content. This is an ideal language skills tool for kids who are psyched by arcade games and don't mind racing the clock.

WORLD ATLAS 5.0

19 16 16 **15**

$$

Mindscape   Win/Mac
Geography/Maps

With multimedia and a "wealth of statistical data," this has all the makings of a world class reference, but *World Atlas* doesn't quite make it. Although there's a lot here, including 150 videos, photos, language lessons with audio pronunciations, graphs and more than 60,000 statistics, many maps are "crude," and there are only 47 city maps. If you buy atlases for the maps, get a book instead.

WORLD OF TOTTY PIG

17 19 19 19

Ages: 3-8 $$

Byron Preiss Multimedia Company, Inc. Win/Mac
Kids/Stories

Kids will squeal over this "charming" title and "relate to it immediately." The story brings appropriate, repetitive text to life with "crisp" graphics and good character voices that speak slowly, so kids can follow the highlighted text. Games, puzzles and four original songs add depth. There are some noticeable design flaws. You can't exit screens until narration and animations end, and it could also use "more interactivity." Still, it's a very sweet first reader.

WORLD'S GREATEST SPEECHES

19 16 19 19

$

Softbit, Inc. Win
History

Hear and see Martin Luther King deliver his famous "I Have a Dream" speech. This exhaustive disc gives users access to over 400 of history's most famous speeches. While the bulk of the material is pure text, there are some videos, audios, and still photos. The speeches are diverse, ranging from ancient Greek to modern American. If you are interested in words from humanity's most eloquent minds, this disc will not disappoint.

WRITE WITH ME

19 15 19 18

Ages: 5-9 $$$

WordPerfect Corporation Win
Kids/Art & Writing

This discontinued product will probably linger for a while, but look for price reductions. This is a beginning word processor that lets aspiring authors cut, paste, scroll and choose fonts. Templates generate a diary, book reports, letters, signs and cards to which children add stickers and draw freehand. The age range is well covered; younger users have the ABC book for alphabet stories. Parents appreciate "how easy it is" for kids and "the fact that it talks."

WYATT EARP'S OLD WEST

14 17 13 14

$$

Grolier Electronic Publishing, Inc. Win/Mac
History

Nice graphics mark this history-rich title on the legend of Dodge City. This "tour of Tombstone" gives users a good "general sense" of the Old West. Looking around the little city, you'll read numerous descriptions of places such as China Alley, in this "interesting and unexpected nod to multicultural issues" of the era. But the "simple" shoot-em-up that's included offers "little challenge or lasting value" and users "lose interest in the games and animations quickly."

	C	M	U	O

X-COM: TERROR FROM THE DEEP
23 22 22 23
$$
MicroProse Software, Inc.   DOS
Games/Combat
An eerie sequel to the original X-Com, this time your aqua-
nauts are plagued by invaders under the waves. Study the
aliens, develop technologies to counter theirs, and then
send your squad into turn-based combat. While it can't
boast of groundbreaking graphics or intense action, this is
"one of the best strategy games available." You'll spend as
much time managing resources and training soldiers as
you do in battle. "Highly addictive."

X-MEN CARTOON MAKER
– – – 18
$$
Knowledge Adventure   Win
Kids/Art & Writing
Guide your team of gifted superhuman mutants through
panel upon panel of "colorful" and "well-drawn" car-
toons. Much like its sister product *Spider-Man Cartoon
Maker*, this disc earns kudos for its "ease of use" and
"interactivity." The disc allows kids to program every step
of the animation, making it as complex or as simple as they
want. The graphics, backgrounds, sounds, and animated
figures are all well-done and easy to manipulate. A must
for true X-Men fans.

X-WING COLLECTOR CD-ROM
19 20 18 19
$$$
LucasArts Entertainment Co.   Win/Mac/DOS
Games/Combat
Too bad the Force can't help install this *Star Wars* game;
there's entirely "too much memory tweaking" and boot
disking before the fun starts. But once you "get the hang of
the touchy controls," you'll "be hooked." The package not
only includes enhanced-graphics versions of the previ-
ously released X-Wing packages—*B-Wing* and *Imperial
Pursuit*—but several new missions to boot. While every-
thing looks spiffier than before, study the manual, because
successfully flying the missions is no easier.

XPLORA 1: PETER GABRIEL'S SECRET WORLD
18 21 15 17
$$$
Interplay Productions   Win/Mac
Music/Interactive Albums
Listen to Peter Gabriel's music, read his lyrics, watch four
music videos, even remix a single. Sounds great, but while
some rave, many found this product "dated," the interface
"obscure" and complain it's "a sell job for his albums."
And there are glitches, such as constant stops and starts in
the music video section. There's lots here for a true fan,
though if you're not interested in Gabriel and his political
causes, the videos are "cool" but even better on MTV.

YOUR MUTUAL FUND SELECTOR   20 16 17 **19**

Intuit
$$
Win

Finance

Video vignettes introduce each of eight chapters in this interactive approach to conservative investing. A vast improvement over typical financial planning worksheets, this helps you choose investments based on your needs. The list of Morningstar's top 1000 funds is somewhat "out-of-date," and would benefit from access to on-line updates, but *Selector's* "informative" and "sophisticated" format makes for "one of the most useful financial CDs" available.

YOUR PERSONAL TRAINER   21 15 20 **21**
FOR THE SAT, VERSION 2.0
$$
Davidson & Associates, Inc.   Win/Mac

Test Preparation

Using a clever sports training metaphor for background, you'll be doing 'workouts' and having a 'coach' train you for the SAT. Advice and encouragement are offered along the way as you're put through your paces on every aspect of the test. (The pointer even turns into a working #2 pencil to simulate the test experience!) A very useful tutorial—despite a "stupid" study game and "almost no multimedia"—for preparing college-bound students for this major exam.

YOUR PORTFOLIO INTERACTIVE   15 15 17 **17**
$
Compton's NewMedia   Win

Finance

This title teaches investing basics by letting you build and track a hypothetical portfolio from 100 mutual funds. It covers such things as simple risk analysis and asset allocation. Unfortunately, mutual fund data is outdated, and you can't easily sift the funds for specific information. Though there's a for-fee online link to Reuters Money Network, this link is static, and doesn't permanently update the mutual funds database. When you're in the time-sensitive world of investing, this title "doesn't have staying power."

YUKON TRAIL   19 19 20 **19**

Ages: 10-16 $$
MECC   Win/Mac

Kids/Edugames-Social Studies

Get the pick and the sieve, and get ready to find some gold! This "good educational" game is most appropriate for pre-teens and teens, leading them on a winding nineteenth-century journey from Seattle to the Yukon. Buy supplies, navigate through the terrain and cull advice from folks along the way. But be careful! It's as "real to life" as it gets, and the wrong choice can leave you broke— or worse...

ZEPHYR

17 18 13 **16**

$$

New World Computing, Inc.   DOS
Games/Action

Racing around a futuristic city in a hovercraft, blasting away at other flying tanks, is a trip once you get the hang of it. But the "cool graphics" turn into sensory overload that can make "what seems like millions of enemy ships" appear indistinguishable from advertising billboards. Eventually this shooter grows on you, but have you got the patience? And can you tweak your PC to make it run in the first place?

ZEPPELIN!

9 12 9 **8**

$

MicroProse Software, Inc.   DOS
Games/Simulation

A "clever idea" miserably executed. Invest $2 million in a blimp, fly between cities to increase earnings and set speed records, establish profitable routes and build more ships. But like the agonizingly slow airships, this "boring sepia-colored" game drags on "even on a Pentium 90 with quad-speed drive." To make matters worse, the manual is inadequate, the annoying Wagnerian soundtrack can't be turned off without turning off the digitized speech, and... what else is there to say?

ZURK'S RAINFOREST LAB: LIFE SCIENCE AND MATH

15 15 15 **15**

Ages: 5-9 $$

Soleil Software   Win/Mac
Kids/Science

"Gorgeous graphics" and "fun puzzles" don't hide the fact that Zurk's Rainforest Lab is operating under false pretenses: no lab, and little Rainforest. The "inventive" interface, a jungle marketplace, leads kids to games and puzzles that teach life sciences, writing and geometry skills. Or, they can choose the "moderately educational" jungle guide, which unfortunately "lacks information" about the environment or botany. Kids might enjoy a visit, but they won't get lost in this "limited" forest.

21ST CENTURY ENTERTAINMENT, INC.
P.O. Box 415
Webster, NY 14580
(716) 872-1200

3M LEARNING SOFTWARE
3M Center, Building 223-5N-01
Saint Paul, MN 55144-1000
(612) 733-1880

4HOME PRODUCTIONS
One Computer Associates Plaza
Islandia, NY 11788-7000
(516) 342-2000

7TH LEVEL
5225 San Fernando Road
W. Los Angeles, CA 90039
(818) 547-1955

A.D.A.M. SOFTWARE, INC
1600 River Edge Parkway, Suite 800
Atlanta, GA 30328
(800) 755-2326

ACCESS SOFTWARE, INC
4910 W. Amelia Earhart Drive
Salt Lake City, UT 84116
(801) 359-2900

ACCLAIM
One Acclaim Plaza
Glen Cove, NY 11542-2708
(516) 656-5000

ACCOLADE, INC
5300 Stevens Creek Blvd., Suite 500
San Jose, CA 95129
(408) 985-1700

ACTIVISION
11601 Wilshire Boulevard, Suite 1000
Los Angeles, CA 90025
(310) 473-9200

AGAINST ALL ODDS PRODUCTIONS
P.O. Box 1189
Sausalito, CA 94966
(415) 331-6300

AHEAD
19A Crosby Drive, Suite 300
Bedford, MA 01730-1419
(617) 271-0900

ALLEGRO NEW MEDIA
16 Passaic Avenue, Bldg. 6
Fairfield, NJ 07004
(800) 424-1992

AMERICAN BUSINESS INFORMATION, INC
Optical Products Division, 5711 S. 86th Circle
Omaha, NE 68127
(402) 593-4595

AMERICAN LASER GAMES
4801 Lincoln Road NE
Albuquerque, NM 87109
(505) 880-1718

AMTEX SOFTWARE CORPORATION
P.O. Box 572
Belleville, Ontario K8N 5B2
(613) 967-7900

APOGEE SOFTWARE
P.O. Box 496389
Garland, TX 75049
(800) 276-4331

APPLE COMPUTER, INC
One Infinite Loop
Cupertino, CA 95014
(408) 996-1010

ARNOWITZ STUDIOS
One Harbor Drive, #200
Sausalito, CA 94965
(415) 332-5555

AROME INTERACTIVE
1430 Bidwell Ave.
Chico, CA 95926
(916) 891-0557

ATTICA CYBERNETICS LTD.
9234 Deering Avenue
Chatsworth, CA 91311
(800) 721-2475

BANNER BLUE SOFTWARE
39500 Stevenson Place, Suite 204
Fremont, CA 94539
(510) 794-6850

BAYWARE INC
P.O. Box 5554
San Mateo, CA 94402
(415) 286-4480

BIG TOP PRODUCTIONS
548 4th Street
San Francisco, CA 94107
(415) 978-5363

BLIZZARD ENTERTAINMENT
3152 Red Hill Avenue, Suite 230
Costa Mesa, CA 92626
(800) 953-7669

BOOKS THAT WORK
2300 Geng Road, Bldg. 3, Suite 100
Palo Alto, CA 94303
(415) 843-4400

BRODERBUND SOFTWARE, INC
500 Redwood Boulevard
Novato, CA 94948-6121
(415) 382-4400

BUNGIE SOFTWARE
1935 S. Halsted St., Suite 204
Chicago, IL 60608-3454
(312) 563-6200

BUREAU OF ELECTRONIC PUBLISHING
141 New Road
Parsippany, NJ 07054
(201) 808-2700

BYRON PREISS MULTIMEDIA COMPANY, INC
24 West 25th Street, 10th Floor
New York, NY 10010
(212) 989-6252

CAMBRIX PUBLISHING
6269 Variel Avenue, Suite B
Woodland Hills, CA 91367
(818) 992-8484

CANTER TECHNOLOGY
101 Commonwealth Avenue
San Francisco, CA 94118
(415)387-0400

CLARIS CORP.
5201 Patrick Henry Drive
Santa Clara, CA 95052-8168
(415) 513-0976

CLIFFS STUDYWARE
P.O. Box 80728
Lincoln, NE 68501-0728
(402) 423-5050

COMPACT PUBLISHING, INC
5141 MacArthur Blvd.
Washington, DC 20016
(202) 244-4770

COMPTON'S NEWMEDIA
2320 Camino Vida Roble
Carlsbad, CA 92009
(619) 929-2500

CONEXUS, INC
5252 Balboa Avenue, Suite 605
San Diego, CA 92117
(619) 268-3380

CORBIS PUBLISHING
15395 SE 30th Place, Suite 300
Bellevue, WA 98007
(206) 649-3307

COREL CORPORATION
1600 Carling Way
Ottawa, Ontario K1Z 8R7 Canada
(613) 728-8200

CREATIVE LABS
1901 McCarthy Blvd.
Milpitas, CA 95035
(408) 426-6600

CREATIVE MULTIMEDIA CORPORATION
513 Northwest 13th Avenue, Suite 400
Portland, OR 97209
(503) 241-4351

CREATIVE WONDERS
c/o Electronic Arts, P.O. Box 7530
San Mateo, CA 94404-2064
(415) 513-7555

CYAN, INC
P.O. Box 28096
Spokane, WA 99228
(509) 468-0807

CYBERDREAMS
23586 Calabasas Road, Suite 102
Calabasas, CA 91302 USA
(818) 223-9990

CYBERFLIX, INC
4 Market Square
Knoxville, TN 37902
(615) 546-1157

D.C. HEATH AND CO.
125 Spring Street
Lexington, MA 02173 USA
(617) 862-6650

DAVIDSON & ASSOCIATES, INC
19840 Pioneer Ave.
Torrance, CA 90503
(310) 793-0600

DEEP RIVER PUBLISHING
P.O. Box 9715-975
Portland, ME 04104
(800) 643-5630

DELORME MAPPING SYSTEMS
P. O. Box 298
Freeport, ME 04032
(207) 865-1234

DELRINA CORPORATION
895 Don Mills Road, 500-2 Park Centre
Toronto, Ontario M3C 1W3 Canada
(800) 268-6082

DIAMAR INTERACTIVE CORPORATION
600 University Street, 1701 One Union Square
Seattle, WA 98101-1129
(206)340-5975

DIGITAL DIRECTORY ASSISTANCE, INC
5161 River Road, Building 6
Bethesda, MD 20816
(800) 284-8353

DIGITAL PICTURES INC
1825 South Grant Street, Suite 900
San Mateo, CA 94402
(415)345-5300

DISCIS KNOWLEDGE RESEARCH, INC
90 Sheppard Avenue East, 7th Floor
Toronto, Ontario M2N 3A1 Canada
(416) 250-6537

DISCOVERY HOME ENTERTAINMENT
7700 Wisconsin Avenue
Bethesda, MD 20814-3579
(301) 986-0444

DISNEY INTERACTIVE
500 South Buena Vista Street
Burbank, CA 91521
(818) 543-4380

DOMARK SOFTWARE, INC.
1900 S. Norfolk Street, Suite 110
San Mateo, CA 94403
(415)513-8929

DORLING KINDERSLEY PUBLISHING, INC.
95 Madison Avenue
New York, NY 10016
(212) 213-4800

DOW JONES & COMPANY
Business Information Services, P.O. Box 300
Princeton, NJ 08543-0300
(609) 520-4000

DR. T'S MUSIC SOFTWARE
124 Crescent Rd.
Needham, MA 02194
(617)455-1454

EA SPORTS
1450 Fashion Island Road
San Mateo, CA 94404
(415) 571-7171

EDMARK CORPORATION
6727 185th Ave. NE
Redmond, WA 98073
(206) 556-8400

ELECTRONIC ARTS
1450 Fashion Island Blvd.
San Mateo, CA 94404
(415) 571-7171

ENCYCLOPAEDIA BRITANNICA EDUCATIONAL CORP
Britannica Centre, 310 S. Michigan Ave.
Chicago, IL 60604
(312) 347-7350

EXPERT SOFTWARE
800 Douglas Road
Coral Gables, FL 33134-3160
(305) 567-9990

FAIRFIELD LANGUAGE TECHNOLOGIES
122 South Main Street
Harrisonburg, VA 22801
(703) 432-6166

FOLLGARD CD VISIONS, INC.
6110 C-1A Street SW
Calgary, Alberta T2H 0G3 Canada
(800) 721-1142

GAMETEK, INC
2999 Northeast 191 St., Suite 500
Aventura, FL 33180
(305) 935-3995

GRAFICA MULTIMEDIA
1777 Borel Place, Suite 500
San Mateo, CA 94402
(415) 358-5555

GRAPHIX ZONE
38 Corporate Park, Suite 100
Irvine, CA 92714
(714) 833-3838

GREEN THUMB SOFTWARE
75 Manhattan Drive, Suite 100
Boulder, CO 80303
(303) 499-1388

GROLIER ELECTRONIC PUBLISHING, INC
Sherman Turnpike
Danbury, CT 06816
(203) 797-3500

GT INTERACTIVE SOFTWARE
16 East 40th Street
New York, NY 10016
(212) 951-3158

GTE INTERACTIVE MEDIA
2385 Camino Vida Roble, Suite 200
Carlsbad, CA 92009
(619) 431-8801

HARPERCOLLINS INTERACTIVE
Advanced Media Group, 10 E. 53 St.
New York, NY 10022-5299
(212) 207-7000

HEADBONE INTERACTIVE INC.
1520 Bellevue Avenue
Seattle, WA 98122
(206) 323-0073

HI TECH ENTERTAINMENT, INC
584 Broadway
New York, NY 10012
(800) 216-1750

HUMONGOUS ENTERTAINMENT
16932 Woodinville-Redmond Rd. NE
Woodinville, WA 98072
(206) 486-9258

HYPER-QUEST, INC.
1718 Main Street, Suite 333
Sarasota, FL 34236
(813) 365-9800

HYPERBOLE STUDIOS
111 N. Hollywood Way
Burbank, CA 91505
(818) 840-6329

HYPERGLOT SOFTWARE COMPANY, INC.
P.O. Box 10746
Knoxville, TN 37939-0746
(800) 800-8270

I-MOTION, INC.
1341 Ocean Ave., Box 417
Santa Monica, CA 90401
(800) 443-3386

IBM MULTIMEDIA STUDIO
1500 Riveredge Parkway, 2nd Floor
Atlanta, GA 30328
(800) 898-8842

IMPRESSIONS SOFTWARE, INC.
222 Third Street, Suite 0234
Cambridge, MA 02142
(617) 225-0500

INDIVIDUAL SOFTWARE INCORPORATED
5870 Stoneridge Drive, Suite #1
Pleasanton, CA 94588-9900
(800) 331-3313

INROADS INTERACTIVE
1050 Walnut Street Suite 301
Boulder, CO 80302
(303) 444-0632

INSCAPE
1933 Pontius Avenue
Los Angeles, CA 90025
(310) 312-5705

INTELLIMEDIA SPORTS, INC
Two Piedmont Center, Suite 300
Atlanta, GA 30305
(404) 262-0000

INTERMEDIA INTERACTIVE STUDIOS
3624 Market Street, #302
Philadelphia, PA 19104
(215) 387-0448

INTERPLAY PRODUCTIONS
17922 Fitch Ave.
Irvine, CA 92714
(714) 553-6655

INTUIT
P.O. Box 3014
Menlo Park, CA 94025
(800) 624-8742

ION PRODUCTIONS
11845 Olympic Boulevard, Suite 1050
Los Angeles, CA 90099-3835
(310) 312-8060

ISM, INC.
201 West Padonia Road, Suite 200
Timonium, MD 21093
(410)560-0973

IVI, INC
7500 Flying Cloud Dr.
Minneapolis, MN 55344-3739
(612) 996-6000

JASMINE MULTIMEDIA PUBLISHING, INC
6746 Valjean Avenue, Suite 100
Van Nuys, CA 91406
(818) 780-3344

JOSTENS HOME LEARNING
9920 Pacific Heights Boulevard, #100
San Diego, CA 92121-4430
(800) 521-8538

KNOWLEDGE ADVENTURE
4502 Dyer St.
La Crescenta, CA 91214
(818) 542-4200

LASER RESOURCES, INC
20620 South Leapwood Avenue, Bldg. F
Carson, CA 90746
(800) 535-2737

LIFESTYLE SOFTWARE GROUP
63 Orange Street
St. Augustine, FL 32084-3584
(904) 825-0220

LIVE OAK MULTIMEDIA
5901 Christie Avenue, #102
Emeryville, CA 94608
(510)654-7480

LIVING BOOKS
500 Redwood Boulevard
Novato, CA 94948-6121
(415) 352-5200

LOGOS RESEARCH SYSTEMS
2117 200th Avenue West
Oak Harbor, WA 98277
(360) 679-6575

LUCASARTS ENTERTAINMENT CO.
P.O. Box 10307
San Rafael, CA 94912
(415) 721-3300

LYRIQ INTERNATIONAL CORPORATION
1701 Highland Avenue, #4
Cheshire, CT 06410
(203) 250-2070

MARIS MULTIMEDIA
100 Smith Ranch Road, Suite 301
San Rafael, CA 94903
(415) 492-2819

MASQUE PUBLISHING
P.O. Box 5223
Englewood, CO 80155
(303) 290-9853

MAXIS
2 Theatre Square, Suite 230
Orinda, CA 94563-3346
(510) 254-9700

MECC
6160 Summit Drive North
Minneapolis, MN 55430-4003
(800) 685-6322

MEDIA DESIGN INTERACTIVE
The Old Hop Kiln, 1 Long Garden Walk
Farnham, Surrey GU9 7HP UK
(+44)1252 737630

MEDIA MOSAIC
1314 Northwest Irving Street, Suite 713
Portland, OR 97209-2728
(503) 225-1988

MEDIO MULTIMEDIA INC
2643 151st Place NE
Redmond, WA 98004
(800) 788-3866

MEGATECH SOFTWARE
1606 Lockness Place
Torrance, CA 90501
(310)539-6452

MICROGRAFX
1303 Arapaho Road
Richardson, TX 75081
(214) 994-6368

MICROLEAGUE INTERACTIVE SOFTWARE
750 Dawson Drive
Newark, DE 19713
(800) 334-2722

MICROLOGIC SOFTWARE
1351 Ocean Avenue
Emeryville, CA 94608-1128
(708) 291-1616

MICROPROSE SOFTWARE, INC.
180 Lakefront Drive
Hunt Valley, MD 21030-2245
(800) 879-7529

MICROSOFT CORPORATION
One Microsoft Way
Redmond, WA 98052
(206) 882-8080

MIDISOFT CORP
P.O. Box 1000
Bellevue, WA 98009
(206) 881-7176

MILLENNIUM MEDIA GROUP, INC.
234 North Columbus Boulevard
Philadelphia, PA 19106
(215) 625-8888

MILLER ASSOCIATES
11 Burtis Avenue, Suite 200
New Canaan, CT 06840
(203) 972-0777

MILLIKEN PUBLISHING CO
1100 Research Blvd.
St. Louis, MO 63132
(314) 991-4220

MINDSCAPE
60 Leveroni Court
Novato, CA 94949
(415)883-3000

MNI INTERACTIVE, INC.
501 Second Street, Suite 350
San Francisco, CA 94107
(415) 904-6340

MORGAN INTERACTIVE
160 Pine Street, Suite 509
San Francisco, CA 94111
(115)693-9596

MOST SIGNIFICANT BITS
15508 Madison Ave.
Lakewood, OH 44107
(216) 221-9836

MULTICOM PUBLISHING, INC
1100 Olive Way, Suite 1250
Seattle, WA 98101
(206) 622-5530

NATIONAL GEOGRAPHIC SOCIETY, EDUCATIONAL MEDIA
P.O. Box 98018
Washington, DC 20036-4688
(800) 368-2728

NEW WORLD COMPUTING, INC.
29800 Agoura Road, Suite 200
Agoura Hills, CA 91301
(818) 889-5600

NEWS ELECTRONIC DATA, INC.
28 Center Street
Clinton, NJ 08809
(908) 735-2555

NOVA LOGIC, INC
26010 Mureau Road, Suite 200
Calabasas, CA 91302
(818) 880-1997

OCEAN SOFTWARE LTD.
1870 Little Orchard Street
San Jose, CA 95125
(408) 289-1200

OPCODE INTERACTIVE
3950 Fabian Way, Suite 100
Palo Alto, CA 94303
(415) 494-1112

OPTIMUM RESOURCE, INC
5 Hiltech Lane
Hilton Head, SC 29926
(803) 689-8000

ORIGIN SYSTEMS, INC.
12940 Research Blvd.
Austin, TX 78750
(512) 335-5200

PAPYRUS
35 Medford Street
Somerville, MA 02143
(617)868-5440

PARSONS (INTUIT)
P.O. Box 100
Hiawatha, IA 52233-0100
(319) 395-9626

PHILIPS MEDIA ELECTRONIC PUBLISHING
10960 Wilshire Boulevard, Suite 700
Los Angeles, CA 90024
(310) 444-6500

PHILIPS MEDIA GAMES
10960 Wilshire Boulevard, Suite 700
Los Angeles, CA 90024
(310) 444-6500

PILGRIM NEW MEDIA
955 Massachusetts Avenue
Cambridge, MA 02138
(617)491-7660

PIXEL PERFECT SOFTWARE
10460 South Tropical Trail
Merritt Island, FL 32952
(407) 779-0310

PRO CD, INC.
222 Rosewood Drive
Danvers, MA 01923
(508) 750-0000

PSYGNOSIS, LTD.
675 Massachusetts Avenue
Cambridge, MA 02139
(617) 497-5457

PUTNAM NEW MEDIA
11490 Commerce Park Drive, Suite 130
Reston, VA 22091
(800) 788-6262

RAND McNALLY NEW MEDIA
8255 North Central Park Avenue
Skokie, IL 60076
(800) 671-5006

RANDOM HOUSE NEW MEDIA
201 East 50th Street
New York, NY 10019
(212) 751-2600

REALTIME SPORTS
1120 Avenue of the Americas, 20th Floor
New York, NY 10036
(212) 395-9800

REED INTERACTIVE
20251 Century Boulevard
Germantown, MD 20874-1196
(800) 922-9204

ROMBOY
5200 Lankershim Boulevard
North Hollywood, CA 91601
(818)752-5900

SALES CURVE INTERACTIVE
330 Washington Boulevard, Suite 713
Marina Del Rey, CA 90292
(310)577-1518

SANCTUARY WOODS MULTIMEDIA CORPORATION
1825 South Grant Street
San Mateo, CA 94402
(415) 578-6340

SCIENCE FOR KIDS
P.O Box 519
Lewisville, NC 27023
(800) 572-4362

SIERRA ON-LINE, INC
40033 Sierra Way
Oakhurst, CA 93644
(800) 326-6654

SIMON & SCHUSTER INTERACTIVE
1230 Ave. of the Americas
New York, NY 10020
(212) 698-7000

SIR-TECH SOFTWARE
P.O. Box 245
Ogdensburg, NY 13669
(315) 393-6451

SIRIUS PUBLISHING, INC
7320 East Butherus Drive, Suite 100
Scottsdale, AZ 85260
(602) 951-3288

SOFTBIT, INC.
One Whitewater
Irvine, CA 92715
(714)251-8600

SOFTKEY INTERNATIONAL
1 Athenaeum Place
Cambridge, MA 02142
(617) 494-1200

SOLEIL SOFTWARE
3853 Grove Court
Palo Alto, CA 94303
(415)494-0114

SONY IMAGESOFT
2400 Broadway Avenue, Suite 550
Santa Monica, CA 90404
(310) 449-2999

SOUND SOURCE INTERACTIVE
2985 East Hillcrest Dr., Suite A
Westlake Village, CA 91362
(805) 494-9996

SPECTRUM HOLOBYTE, INC.
2490 Mariner Square Loop
Alameda, CA 94501
(510) 522-3584

STARPRESS MULTIMEDIA
303 Sacramento Street, 2nd Floor
San Francisco, CA 94111
(415) 274-8383

STELLA INTERACTIVE
2185 Faraday Ave., Suite 100
Carlsbad, CA 92008
(619) 431-8221

STORMFRONT STUDIOS
4000 Civic Center Drive, Suite 450
San Rafael, CA 94903
(415) 479-2800

STRATEGIC SIMULATIONS CORPORATION
675 Almanor Avenue, Suite 201
Sunnyvale, CA 94086
(800) 601-7529

SUMERIA INC
329 Bryant Street, Suite 3D
San Francisco, CA 94107
(415) 904-0800

SUNSET NEW MEDIA
80 Willow Road
Menlo Park, CA 94025-3691
(800) 227-7346

SWFTE INTERNATIONAL, LTD.
Box 219
Rockland, DE 19732-9904
(302) 734-1750

SYNERGY INTERACTIVE CORPORATION
333 South Hope Street, Suite 2500
Los Angeles, CA 90071
(213) 687-2905

SYRACUSE LANGUAGE SYSTEMS
719 East Genesee Street
Syracuse, NY 13210
(315) 478-6729

T/MAKER
1390 Villa Street
Mountain View, CA 94041
(415) 962-0195

TAKE 2 INTERACTIVE SOFTWARE, INC.
575 Broadway
New York, NY 10012
(212) 941-2988

THE LEARNING COMPANY
6493 Kaiser Drive
Fremont, CA 94555
(510) 792-9628

TIME-WARNER INTERACTIVE GROUP
675 Sycamore Drive
Milpitas, CA 95035
(408) 434-3700

TIMES MIRROR MULTIMEDIA
4221 Wilshire Blvd., Suite 170
Los Angeles, CA 90010
(213) 930-3100

TRANSPARENT LANGUAGE
22 Proctor Hill Road, P.O. Box 575
Hollis, NH 03049
(800) 752-1767

TRIMARK INTERACTIVE
2644 30th Street
Santa Monica, CA 90405-3009
(310) 314-2000

VELOCITY
Four Embarcadero Center, Suite 3100
San Francisco, CA 94111
(800) 856-2489

VERTIGO DEVELOPMENT GROUP, INC.
58 Charles Street
Cambridge, MA 02141
(617)225-2065

VIACOM INTERACTIVE MEDIA
1515 Broadway
New York, NY 10036
(212) 258-6000

VIDEODISCOVERY, INC
1700 Westlake Ave. N., Suite 600
Seattle, WA 98109-3012
(206) 285-5400

VILLA CRESPO SOFTWARE
1725 McGovern
Highland Park, IL 60035
(708)433-0500

VIRGIN INTERACTIVE ENTERTAINMENT
18061 Fitch Avenue
Irvine, CA 92714
(714) 833-8710

VIRGIN SOUND & VISION
122 South Robertson Boulevard
Los Angeles, CA 90048
(310) 246-4666

VIRTUAL ENTERTAINMENT, INC.
200 Highland Avenue
Needham, MA 02194
(617)449-7567

VIRTUAL REALITY LABORATORIES, INC
2341 Ganador Court
San Luis Obispo, CA 93401
(805) 545-8515

VIRTUAL VEGAS
433 Main Street
Venice, CA 90291
(310) 829-5457

VISUAL SOFTWARE
21731 Venture Blvd., Suite 310
Woodland Hills, CA 91364
(800) 669-7318

VOYAGER COMPANY
578 Broadway, Suite 406
New York, NY 10012
(212)431-5199

WALNUT CREEK CDROM
1547 Palos Verdes Mall, Suite 260
Walnut Creek, CA 94596
(510) 674-0783

WARNERACTIVE
111 North Hollywood Way
Burbank, CA 91505
(818) 840-6329

WILSON LEARNING CORPORATION
7500 Flying Cloud Drive
Eden Prarie, MN 55344
(612) 944-2880

WIZARDWORKS, INC.
3850 Annapolis Ln., Suite 100
Plymouth, MN 55447
(612) 559-5140

WORDPERFECT CORPORATION
Consumer Products Division, 1555 N. Technology Way
Orem, UT 84057-2399
(801) 225-5000

Subject Index
Age Range   Title   Overall Rating

ANATOMY
    See Science/Anatomy

ANIMALS
    See Science/Animals

ANTHOLOGIES
    See Reference/Anthology

ARCADE GAMES
    See Games/Arcade

ART APPRECIATION

	Title	Rating
	American Visions	18
	Art Gallery	21
	Comic Book Confidential	19
	Face of Life	14
	Great Artists	19
	I Photograph to Remember	20
	Passion for Art	21
	Ultimate Frank Lloyd Wright: America's Architect	18

ART TOOLS FOR KIDS
    See Kids/Art & Writing

ASTRONOMY
    See Science/Astronomy

ATLASES
    See Geography/Maps or Travel/Maps & Atlases

AVANT GARDE

	Title	Rating
	Bad Day on the Midway	–
	Freak Show	21
	Gingerbread Man	18
	Headcandy	12
	Meet MediaBand	17
	Puppet Motel	19

COMBAT GAMES
    See Games/Combat

COMICS

Age Range	Title	Rating
	Cartoon History of the Universe	21
	Comic Book Confidential	19
	Complete Maus	18
Ages: 6 & up	Hanna-Barbera Cartoon Carnival	12
	Mask: The Origin	11
	Noctropolis	18
Ages: 5 & up	Spider-Man Cartoon Maker	18
	X-Men Cartoon Maker	18

CONSUMER GUIDES

Automania: The Ultimate Car
    Buying Guide   16
Barron's Profiles of American Colleges   16
Car and Driver '95 Buyer's Guide   16
Clark Howard's Consumer Survival Kit   19
Consumer Reports Cars: The Essential Guide–
Dr. Scheuler Presents The Corner Drugstore   –
Lovejoy's College Counselor   18
MusicNet   21
Popular Mechanics New Car Buyers
    Guide 1995   19

COOKING & FOOD

4 Paws of Crab: An Interactive
Thai Cookbook   20
Art of Making Great Pastries   16
Beauty of Japan Through the Art of Sushi   12
Better Homes and Gardens Healthy
    Cooking CD Cookbook   15
Deal-A-Meal Interactive (Richard Simmons) 15
Food & Wine's Wine Tasting: An
    Interactive Experience   16
Four Seasons of Gourmet French Cuisine   14
Great Restaurants, Wineries & Breweries   12
Julia Child: Home Cooking with
    Master Chefs   21
MasterCook Silver Platter Cookbook   14
Southern Living Cookbook   15
Wine Guide   24
Wines of the World   16

CULTURAL STUDIES

4 Paws of Crab: An Interactive Thai
    Cookbook   20
500 Nations   21
Ages: all   Archibald's Guide to the Mysteries
    of Ancient Egypt   17
Ages: 5-8   Around the World in 80 Days   15
Beauty of Japan Through the Art of Sushi   12
Beyond the Sambatyon: The Myth of the Ten
    Lost Tribes   18
Ages: 8 & up Eagle Eye Mysteries in London   20
From Alice to Ocean: Alone Across the
    Outback   19
Haight-Ashbury in the Sixties   16
Material World: A Global Family Portrait   16
Ages: 11 & up Nile: Passage to Egypt   21
One Tribe   18

Passage to Vietnam   23
Smithsonian's America   18

CURRENT AFFAIRS

Bernard of Hollywood's Marilyn   11
CNN Newsroom Global View   14
Comic Book Confidential   19
Face of Life   14
Haight-Ashbury in the Sixties   16
Haldeman Diaries: Inside the Nixon
    White House   20
Hard Evidence: The Marilyn
    Monroe Files   14
People: 20 Years of Pop Culture   16
Playboy Interviews   18
Rock 'N' Roll Your Own   18
Time Almanac 1995   19
TIME Almanac of the 20th Century   19
Vietnam   21

DESKTOP PUBLISHING
    See Graphics/Desktop Publishing

DICTIONARIES
    See Reference/Dictionaries

EARLY LEARNING SKILLS
    See Kids/Early Learning Skills

ENCYCLOPEDIAS
    See Reference/Encyclopedias

FAMILY

Echo Lake   24
Emily Post's Complete Guide to
    Weddings   15
Family Tree Maker Deluxe CD-ROM
    Edition   22

FINANCE

Jonathan Pond's Personal Financial
    Planner   17
Parents' Guide to Money   20
Plan Ahead for Your Financial Future   16
Quicken Deluxe 4 for Windows   22
Your Mutual Fund Selector   19
Your Portfolio Interactive   17

FIRST PERSON GAMES
    See Games/Role Playing & Interactive Fiction

FOOD & COOKING
    See Cooking & Food

GARDENING
     See House & Garden

GAMES/ACTION

	Title	Rating
	Aliens	–
	Battledrome	12
Ages: 17 & up	Bioforge	19
	Cannon Fodder	16
	Creature Shock	15
	Cyberia	16
Ages: 13 & up	D!Zone Collectors Edition	17
	Dark Forces	23
	Descent	22
	Doom Heaven	15
	Doom II: Hell on Earth	22
Ages: 17 & up	Ecstatica	16
Ages: 13 & up	FX Fighter	17
	Heretic	20
	Hexen: Beyond Heretic	–
	Hi-Octane	20
Ages: 9 & up	I. M. Meen	17
	Iron Assault	12
	Jump Raven	13
	Mad Dog II: The Lost Gold	16
	Magic Carpet	19
	Marathon	19
	Mech Warrior 2	20
Ages: 17 & up	Mortal Kombat 2	19
Ages: 17 & up	Mortal Kombat 3	–
	Quarantine	17
	Rebel Assault	19
	Rebel Assault II	–
	Renegade	16
	Rise of the Robots	12
Ages: 13 & up	Rise of the Triad	17
	Savage Warriors	–
	Super Street Fighter II	16
	System Shock	21
	Ultimate Doom	19
	Wing Commander III: Heart of the Tiger	24
	Wyatt Earp's Old West	14
	X-Wing Collector CD-ROM	19
	Zephyr	16

GAMES/ARCADE

	Arcade Mania	–
	Atari 2600 Action Pack	12
	Atari 2600 Action Pack 2	–
	Battle Beast	–
	Clock Werx	19

	Klik & Play	20
	Lode Runner: The Legend Returns	19
	Mad Dog II: The Lost Gold	16
	Take Your Best Shot	17

GAMES/COMBAT

	1942 Gold: The Pacific Air War	21
	Aces of the Deep	20
	Aces: The Complete Collector's Edition	18
	Armored Fist	16
	Battlecruiser 3000 A.D.	–
	Blue & The Gray	10
	Comanche CD	20
	Command and Conquer	–
	Cyberwar	13
	Daedalus Encounter	19
	Falcon Gold	18
	Front Lines	17
	Journeyman Project Turbo!	19
	Knights of Xentar	15
	Menzoberranzan	19
	Panzer General	20
	Perfect General II	19
	Tank Commander	12
	TFX: Tactical Fighter Experiment	14
	U.S. Navy Fighters	21
	Warcraft: Orcs and Humans	22
	Wings of Glory	19
	Wings Over Europe	18
	X-COM: Terror from the Deep	23

GAMES/MYSTERY

	11th Hour: The Sequel to the 7th Guest	–
	7th Guest	22
Ages: 12 & up	Alone in the Dark 3	14
	Beast Within	–
	Blown Away	17
	Dracula Unleashed	18
Ages: 8 & up	Eagle Eye Mysteries in London	20
Ages: 8 & up	Eagle Eye Mysteries: The Original	19
	Freddy Pharkas: Frontier Pharmacist	14
	Hard Evidence: The Marilyn Monroe Files	14
Ages: 10 & up	Math Blaster Mystery:	
	The Great Brain Robbery	21
	MTV's Club Dead	16
	Panic in the Park	15
	Phantasmagoria	20
Ages: 17 & up	Police Quest IV: Open Season	8
	Police Quest: The Four Most Wanted	15
	ReElect JFK	15

Games/Mystery Continued…

Ripper   –
Sherlock Holmes, Consulting Detective,
   Volumes I - III   16
Under a Killing Moon   22
Ages: 17 & up Voyeur   16
Who Killed Brett Penance?   17
Who Killed Elsbeth Haskard?
   (The Magic Death)   17
Who Killed Sam Rupert?   12
Who Killed Taylor French?   16

GAMES/PARLOR

Chessmaster 4000 Turbo   19
Hodj 'n' Podj   18
Jeopardy!   17
Pinball Illusions   –
Royal Flush   16
Shanghai: Great Moments   19
Trivial Pursuit   13
Virtual Pool   21
Virtual Vegas Volume One Blackjack   15
Wheel of Fortune   15
Wild Cards   13

GAMES/PUZZLE & LOGIC

11th Hour: The Sequel to the 7th Guest   –
7th Guest   22
Ages: 12 & up Alone in the Dark 3   14
Ages: 8 & up   Are You Afraid of the Dark?
The Tale of Orpheo's Curse   15
Bizarre Adventures of Woodruff and the
   Schnibble   17
Blown Away   17
Bureau 13   13
Buried in Time: The Journeyman Project 2   20
Daedalus Encounter   19
Diggers   12
Discworld   21
Flash Traffic: City of Angels   11
Full Throttle   22
Hodj 'n' Podj   18
Incredible Machine 2   21
Incredible Toon Machine   20
Jewels of the Oracle   19
Ages: 6 & up   Kid Vid Grid   17
Lode Runner   19
Ages: 12 & up Lost Mind of Dr. Brain   21
Monty Python's Complete Waste of Time   23
Myst   22
Star Trek 25th Anniversary   14

GAMES/ROLE PLAYING & INTERACTIVE FICTION

	Air Havoc Controller	20
	Aliens	–
Ages: 12 & up	Alone in the Dark 3	14
Ages: 8 & up	Are You Afraid of the Dark?	
	The Tale of Orpheo's Curse	15
Ages: 9-17	Astronomica: The Quest for the Edge of the Universe	15
	Beast Within	–
	Bizarre Adventures of Woodruff and the Schnibble	17
	Blind Date	7
	Blown Away	17
	Bureau 13	13
	Buried in Time: The Journeyman Project 2	20
	Chaos Control	17
	Congo: The Movie – Descent into Zinj	–
	Creature Shock	15
	Cyberia	16
	Cyberwar	13
Ages: 13 & up	D!Zone Collectors Edition	17
	Daedalus Encounter	19
	Dark Eye	–
	Dark Forces	23
	Descent	22
	Dig	–
	Discworld	21
	Dracula Unleashed	18
	Dragon Lore: Code of the Dragon Knights	18
	Earthsiege	18
Ages: 17 & up	Ecstatica	16
	Flash Traffic: City of Angels	11
	Freddy Pharkas: Frontier Pharmacist	14
	Full Throttle	22
	Gadget	19
Ages: 17 & up	Hell: A Cyberpunk Thriller	16
	I Have No Mouth, and I Must Scream	–
	Inherit the Earth	18
	Jewels of the Oracle	19
	Johnny Mnemonic	13
	Journeyman Project Turbo!	19
	King's Quest Collector's Edition	21
	King's Quest VII: The Princeless Bride	18
	Knights of Xentar	15
	Legend of Kyrandia, Book Three: Malcolm's Revenge	17
	Leisure Suit Larry's Greatest Hits ... and Misses	12
	Lords of the Realm	20

Games/Role Playing and Interactive Fiction Continued…

	Lost Eden	20
Ages: 10 & up	Louis Cat Orze: The Mystery of the Queen's Necklace	19
Ages: all	Manhole CD-ROM Masterpiece Edition	17
	Master of Magic	20
	Menzoberranzan	19
	MTV's Beavis and Butt-head in Virtual Stupidity	–
	MTV's Club Dead	16
	Myst	22
	Noctropolis	18
Ages: 10-16	Oregon Trail II	22
	Outpost	19
	Paparazzi! Tales of Tinseltown	17
	Phantasmagoria	20
Ages: 7-12	Ravenloft: The Stone Prophet	17
	Recess in Greece	20
	ReElect JFK	15
	Relentless: Twinsen's Adventure	22
	Return to Zork	19
	Ripper	–
	Sam & Max Hit the Road	20
	Shadows of Cairn	10
	Sherlock Holmes, Consulting Detective, Volumes I - III	16
	Star Trail	20
	Star Trek 25th Anniversary	14
	Star Trek: The Next Generation "A Final Unity"	19
	Star Trek: The Next Generation Interactive Technical Manual	19
	Synergist	–
	Torin's Passage	–
	Ultimate Domain	16
	Virtual Guitar: Welcome to West Feedback	21
	Vortex: Quantum Gate II	12
	Warcraft: Orcs and Humans	22
	Wing Commander III: Heart of the Tiger	24
Ages: 10-16	Yukon Trail	19

GAMES/SIMULATION

	1942 Gold: The Pacific Air War	21
	Aces of the Deep	20
	Aces: The Complete Collector's Edition	18
	Air Havoc Controller	20
Ages: 10-16	Amazon Trail	20
	Armored Fist	16
	Battledrome	12

Ages: 17 & up	Bioforge	19
	Blue & The Gray	10
	Cannon Fodder	16
	Colonization	19
	Comanche CD	20
	Command and Conquer	–
	Creature Shock	15
	Cyberia	16
	Cyberwar	13
Ages: 13 & up	D!Zone Collectors Edition	17
	Doom Heaven	15
	Doom II: Hell on Earth	22
	Earthsiege	18
	Falcon Gold	18
	Flight Simulator 5.1	22
	Flight Unlimited	22
	Front Lines	17
Ages: 13 & up	FX Fighter	17
	Gadget	19
	Gazillionaire	18
	Gone Fishin'	18
	Heretic	20
	Hexen: Beyond Heretic	–
	High Seas Trader	13
	Iron Assault	12
	Klik & Play	20
	Mech Warrior 2	20
	Outpost	19
	Perfect General II	19
	Pizza Tycoon	13
Ages: 13 & up	Rise of the Triad	17
Ages: 11 & up	SimCity 2000	21
	SimTower	18
Ages: 8-12	SimTown	20
	Tank Commander	12
	TFX: Tactical Fighter Experiment	14
	Transport Tycoon	19
	U.S. Navy Fighters	21
	Ultimate Domain	16
	Wings of Glory	19
	Wings Over Europe	18
	Wolf	16
	Zeppelin!	8

GAMES/SPORTS SIMULATION

	All-Star Baseball	16
	Baseball for Windows - Ernie Harwell	
	Broadcast Blast	19
	Blood Bowl	14
	Brett Hull Hockey '95	17

Games/Sports Simulation Continued…

	Cyclemania	16
	ESPN Baseball Tonight	15
	FIFA Soccer '96	22
	Front Page Sports: Baseball '94	20
	Front Page Sports: Football Pro '95	20
	Front Page Sports: Football Pro '96	–
	Golf	20
	Gone Fishin'	18
	Hardball 4	19
	Hardball 5	20
	IndyCar Racing 2.0	–
	Links 386 CD	21
	Live Action Football	13
	NASCAR Racing	21
	NBA Live '95	21
	NCAA Football	–
	NFL Pro League Football	20
	NHL 96	23
	NHL Hockey 95	18
	PGA Tour Golf '96	20
	PGA Tour Golf 486	19
	Picture Perfect Golf	17
	Quarterback Attack with Mike Ditka	–
	Slam City with Scottie Pippin	14
	Tony LaRussa Baseball 3	19
	Ultimate Football '95	21
	Unnecessary Roughness '95	15
	Unnecessary Roughness '96	–

GENEALOGY/FAMILY HISTORY

	Echo Lake	24
	Family Tree Maker Deluxe	22

GEOGRAPHY/MAPS

Age Range	Title	Rating
Ages: 7 & up	3D Atlas	19
	AAA Trip Planner	14
	Automap Road Atlas	19
	Everywhere USA Travel Guide	15
	Expert Travel Planner	14
	Global Explorer	14
	Map 'n' Go	18
	MapExpert 2.0	18
	Maps 'n' Facts	18
	Material World: A Global Family Portrait	16
	One Tribe	18
	Picture Atlas of the World	16
Ages: 10 & up	Rand McNally Quick Reference Atlas	15
Ages: all	Rand McNally's Children's Atlas of the United States	17

	Rand McNally's Tripmaker	19
Ages: 12 & up	Small Blue Planet: The Cities Below	17
	Small Blue Planet: The Real Picture World Atlas	18
	Street Atlas USA 2.0	20
Ages: 8 & up	Travelrama USA	13
Ages: 9 & up	Where in the USA is Carmen Sandiego?	21
Ages: 9 & up	Where in the World is Carmen Sandiego?	22
Ages: 5-8	Where in the World is Carmen Sandiego? Junior Detective Edition	20
	World Atlas 5.0	15

GRAPHICS/DESKTOP PUBLISHING

	CardShop Plus! Deluxe	21
Ages: 7 & up	Print Artist	20
	Print Shop Deluxe CD Ensemble	22
	PrintMaster Gold CD Bonus Pack	19
	Simply 3D	17
	Sports Illustrated Swimsuit Calendar	11
Ages: 5-9	Write with Me	18

HEALTH/FITNESS

	Deal-A-Meal Interactive (Richard Simmons)	15
	Mayo Clinic Family Health Book	16
	Mayo Clinic Sports Health & Fitness	15

HISTORY

	500 Nations	21
Ages: 10-16	Amazon Trail	20
	America's Civil War: A Nation Divided	11
	Ancient Lands	20
Ages: all	Archibald's Guide to the Mysteries of Ancient Egypt	17
	Beyond the Sambatyon: The Myth of the Ten Lost Tribes	18
	Campaigns, Candidates & the Presidency	18
	Cartoon History of the Universe	21
	Complete Maus	18
	Compton's Encyclopedia of American History	19
	Dead Sea Scrolls Revealed	16
	Earthquake	14
	Haight-Ashbury in the Sixties	16
	Haldeman Diaries: Inside the Nixon White House	20
	Hard Evidence: The Marilyn Monroe Files	14
	Her Heritage: A Biographical Encyclopedia of Famous American Women	18
	House Divided: The Lincoln-Douglas Debates	19

History Continued…

	Ideas That Changed the World	15
	Jazz: A Multimedia History	13
	JFK Assassination: A Visual Investigation	21
	Leonardo the Inventor	16
	Lost Treasures of the World	19
Ages: 10 & up	Louis Cat Orze: The Mystery of the Queen's Necklace	19
Ages: 7 & up	Mario's Time Machine Deluxe	15
Ages: 11 & up	Nile: Passage to Egypt	21
Ages: 10-16	Oregon Trail II	22
	Presidents: A Picture History of Our Nation	12
Ages: 7-12	Recess in Greece	20
	ReElect JFK	15
	Smithsonian's America	18
Ages: 10 & up	Stephen Biesty's Incredible Cross-Sections Stowaway	21
	TIME Almanac of the 20th Century	19
	Vietnam	21
	Who Built America?	20
	World's Greatest Speeches	19
	Wyatt Earp's Old West	14
Ages: 10-16	Yukon Trail	19

HISTORY/WAR

	America's Civil War: A Nation Divided	11
	Blue & The Gray	10
	Complete Maus	18
	House Divided: The Lincoln-Douglas Debates	19
	Vietnam	21
	Warplanes: Modern Flying Aircraft	18
	Wings of Glory	19
	Wings Over Europe	18

HOUSE & GARDEN

	3D Deck	18
	3D Home Architect	20
	3D Landscape	19
	Better Homes and Gardens Complete Guide to Gardening	14
	Home Repair Encyclopedia	19
	Hometime Weekend Home Projects	20
	LandDesigner Multi-Media for Gardens	18
	Simply House	14
	Western Garden	17

HUMOR

	Freddy Pharkas: Frontier Pharmacist	14
	Monty Python's Complete Waste of Time	23

	MTV's Beavis and Butt-head in Virtual Stupidity	–
	Saturday Night Live: The First Twenty Years	13
	Take Your Best Shot	17

INTERACTIVE FICTION
See Games/Role Playing & Interactive Fiction

KIDS/ART & WRITING

Ages: 5-12	Amazing Animation	19
Ages: 6-12	Amazing Writing Machine	21
Ages: 3-6	Crayola Amazing Art Adventure	19
Ages: 6-12	Crayola Art Studio	17
Ages: 8-14	Creative Writer	19
Ages: 3 & up	EA* Kids Art Center	17
Ages: 8-14	Fine Artist	21
Ages: 8 & up	Flying Colors	21
Ages: 3 & up	Imagination Express	19
Ages: 4-10	Kid Works 2	17
Ages: 3-12	KidPix Studio	22
Ages: 7 & up	Print Artist	20
Ages: 5 & up	Spider-Man Cartoon Maker	18
Ages: 5-8	Storybook Maker	16
Ages: 6-12	Storybook Weaver Deluxe	21
Ages: 10 & up	Student Writing & Research Center	21
Ages: 10 & up	Student Writing Center	22
Ages: 4-7	Wiggins in Storyland	17
Ages: 3-6	WiggleWorks	21
Ages: 5-9	Write with Me	18
	X-Men Cartoon Maker	18

KIDS/EARLY LEARNING SKILLS

Ages: 3-8	Allie's Activity Kit	17
Ages: 3-8	Allie's Playhouse	20
Ages: 3-6	Alphabet Blocks	21
Ages: 3 & up	AlphaBonk Farm	17
Ages: 2-6	Bailey's Book House	19
Ages: 3-7	Beginning Reading	21
Ages: 3-7	Busytown	18
Ages: 3-7	Dr. Seuss's ABC	23
Ages: 3-5	Fisher-Price ABC's	17
Ages: 3-8	Hello Kitty Big Fun Deluxe	18
Ages: 3-6	How Many Bugs in a Box?	19
Ages: 3-6	How Things Work in Busytown	19
Ages: 4-6	Jump Start Kindergarten	22
Ages: 3-6	Playroom	16
Ages: 3-6	Sesame Street: Letters	18

Kids/Early Learning Skills Continued…

Ages: 4-6	Sound It Out Land 1	19
Ages: 4-6	Sound It Out Land 2	19
Ages: 4-6	Sound It Out Land 3	18
Ages: 2-6	Stickybear Preschool	9

KIDS/EDUGAMES-GENERAL

Ages: 5 & up	Aladdin Activity Center	20
Ages: 6-10	Anno's Learning Games	17
Ages: 3-7	Busytown	18
	Casper Brainy Book	19
Ages: 3-7	Fatty Bear's Birthday Surprise	15
Ages: 4-9	Freddi Fish and the Case of the Missing Kelp Seeds	20
Ages: 3 & up	Gus Goes to Cyberopolis	10
Ages: 3-7	Gus Goes to Cybertown	16
Ages: 3-6	How Things Work in Busytown	19
Ages: 5-7	Jump Start First Grade	23
Ages: 4-6	Jump Start Kindergarten	22
Ages: 5-11	Lenny's Multimedia Circus	18
Ages: 8-12	Mario is Missing!	11
Ages: 3-8	Mixed-Up Mother Goose	18
Ages: 7-14	Morgan's Trivia Machine	17
Ages: 3-8	Putt-Putt and Fatty Bear's Activity Pack	19
Ages: 3-7	Putt-Putt Goes to the Moon	19
Ages: 3-7	Putt-Putt Joins the Parade	20
Ages: 3-7	Putt-Putt Saves the Zoo	19
Ages: 8-12	SimTown	20
Ages: 4-8	Thinkin' Things, Collection 1	20
Ages: 6-12	Thinkin' Things, Collection 2	22
Ages: 5-9	Treasure Cove!	18
Ages: 4-9	Where's Waldo? at the Circus	19
Ages: 2-7	Why Do We Have To?	13
Ages: 4-7	Wiggins in Storyland	17

KIDS/EDUGAMES-MATH

Ages: 12 & up	Alge-Blaster 3	17
Ages: 5-8	Bit-Bot's Math Voyage	19
Ages: 8-11	Counting on Frank	16
Ages: 10 & up	Cruncher	18
Ages: 3-6	Early Math	18
Ages: 3-5	Fisher-Price 1-2-3's	10
Ages: 6-12	Math Blaster 1: In Search of Spot	22
Ages: 8-13	Math Blaster 2: The Secret of the Lost City	19
Ages: 10 & up	Math Blaster Mystery: The Great Brain Robbery	21
Ages: 4-7	Math Rabbit	18

Subject Index

Age Range	Title	Overall Rating
Ages: 6-12	Math Workshop	22
Ages: 8-14	Memphis Math: Treasure of the Tombs	19
Ages: 3-6	Millie's Math House	20
Ages: 3-6	Sesame Street: Numbers	12
Ages: 7-10	Super Solvers OutNumbered!	17
Ages: 5-9	Treasure Galaxy!	19
Ages: 5-9	Treasure MathStorm!	19
Ages: 6-8	Treasure Mountain!	18
Ages: 6-12	Troggle Trouble Math	16
Ages: 4-9	Where's Waldo? at the Circus	19

Kids/Edugames-Reading

Age Range	Title	Overall Rating
Ages: 9-14	Alien Tales	20
Ages: 3-6	Alphabet Blocks	21
Ages: 3 & up	AlphaBonk Farm	17
Ages: 3-7	Beginning Reading	21
Ages: 3-8	Big Bug Alphabet Book	12
Ages: 3-7	Dr. Seuss's ABC	23
Ages: 4-8	Get Ready For School, Charlie Brown!	–
Ages: 9 & up	I. M. Meen	17
Ages: 4-7	Kid Phonics	20
Ages: 3-7	Read with Me 1 & 2	18
Ages: 3-6	Reader Rabbit 1	18
Ages: 5-8	Reader Rabbit 2	21
Ages: 6-9	Reader Rabbit 3	19
Ages: 3-7	Reader Rabbit's Interactive Reading Journey	20
Ages: 5-7	Reader Rabbit's Reading Development Library, Level 1	22
Ages: 5-7	Reader Rabbit's Reading Development Library, Level 2	22
Ages: 7-10	Reading Blaster: Invasion of the Word Snatchers	20
Ages: 3-6	Sesame Street: Let's Make a Word	18
Ages: 3-6	Sesame Street: Letters	18
Ages: 4-6	Sound It Out Land 1	19
Ages: 4-6	Sound It Out Land 2	19
Ages: 4-6	Sound It Out Land 3	18
Ages: 3-6	WiggleWorks	21
Ages: 10 & up	Word Attack 3	20
Ages: 7-14	Word City	18

Kids/Edugames-Science

Age Range	Title	Overall Rating
Ages: 7-14	Adventures of Hyperman	17
Ages: 5-14	Adventures with Oslo: Tools and Gadgets	18
Ages: 8 & up	AnnaTommy: An Adventure into the Human Body	11
Ages: 4-10	Body Park	14

Kids/Edugame-Science Continued...

Ages: 14 & up	Distant Suns: Desktop Planetarium	17
Ages: 12 & up	Lost Mind of Dr. Brain	21
Ages: 6-10	Magic School Bus Explores the Human Body	19
Ages: 6-10	Magic School Bus Explores the Solar System	20
Ages: 4 & up	Professor Iris' Fun Field Trip: Animal Safari	12
Ages: all	Rand McNally Children's Atlas of World Wildlife	12
Ages: 2-5	Sammy's Science House	21
Ages: 12 & up	Science Sleuths, Volume 1	20
Ages: 12 & up	Science Sleuths, Volume 2	19
Ages: 7-12	Super Solvers Gizmos & Gadgets!	22
	Ultimate Human Body	20
Ages: 5-12	Undersea Adventure	18
Ages: 8-12	What's the Secret?	19
Ages: 8 & up	Widget Workshop	18

KIDS/EDUGAMES-SOCIAL STUDIES

Ages: 10-16	Amazon Trail	20
Ages: 5-8	Around the World in 80 Days	15
Ages: 8 & up	Eagle Eye Mysteries in London	20
Ages: 8 & up	Eagle Eye Mysteries: The Original	19
Ages: 6-10	Explorapedia: The World of People	19
	Ideas That Changed the World	15
Ages: 10 & up	Louis Cat Orze: The Mystery of the Queen's Necklace	19
Ages: 7 & up	Mario's Time Machine Deluxe	15
Ages: 10-16	Oregon Trail II	22
Ages: 7-12	Recess in Greece	20
Ages: 8 & up	Travelrama USA	13
Ages: 9 & up	Where in the USA is Carmen Sandiego?	21
Ages: 9 & up	Where in the World is Carmen Sandiego?	22
Ages: 5-8	Where in the World is Carmen Sandiego? Junior Detective Edition	20
Ages: 10-16	Yukon Trail	19

KIDS/EDUGAMES-SPELLING

Ages: 3-8	Big Bug Alphabet Book	12
Ages: 3-5	Fisher-Price ABC's	17
Ages: 4-8	Get Ready For School, Charlie Brown!	–
Ages: 3-6	Sesame Street: Let's Make a Word	18
Ages: 7-10	Spelling Jungle	21
Ages: 7-12	Super Solvers Spellbound!	18
Ages: 10 & up	Word Attack 3	20
Ages: 7-14	Word City	18

SUBJECT INDEX

Age Range	Title	Overall Rating

KIDS/GENERAL

	Barbie and Her Magical House	19
Ages: 8 & up	Gahan Wilson's The Ultimate Haunted House	19
Ages: 6 & up	Hanna-Barbera Cartoon Carnival	12
Ages: 7 & up	Kid CAD	15
Ages: 6 & up	Kid Vid Grid	17
Ages: 6-10	Kids on Site	16
Ages: 3-9	Lion King Animated Storybook	18
	Lost Eden	20
Ages: all	Manhole CD-ROM Masterpiece Edition	17
Ages: 5 & up	Mario Teaches Typing	18
Ages: 9 & up	Mavis Beacon Teaches Typing for Kids	14
Ages: 10 & up	Student Writing & Research Center	21
Ages: 10 & up	Student Writing Center	22

KIDS/MUSIC

Ages: 3-8	Chuck Jones' Peter and the Wolf	18
Ages: 3-9	CyberBoogie! with Sharon, Lois & Bram	14
Ages: 3-10	Dr. T's Sing-A-Long Around the World	20
Ages: 3-10	Dr. T's Sing-A-Long Kids Classics	17
Ages: 5-11	KidRiffs	16
Ages: 7 & up	Lenny's MusicToons	18
	Midisoft Music Mentor Maestro Edition	14
	Musical Instruments	23
Ages: 5 & up	Stradiwackius: The Counting Concert	16
Ages: 3 & up	TuneLand	20

KIDS REFERENCE
See Reference/Kids

KIDS/SCIENCE

Ages: 7 & up	3-D Body Adventure	19
Ages: 3 & up	3-D Dinosaur Adventure	15
Ages: 7-14	Adventures of Hyperman	17
Ages: 5-14	Adventures with Oslo: Tools and Gadgets	18
Ages: 8 & up	AnnaTommy: An Adventure into the Human Body	11
Ages: 9-17	Astronomica: The Quest for the Edge of the Universe	15
Ages: 8 & up	Aviation Adventure	14
Ages: 3-8	Bug Adventure	19
Ages: 6 & up	Coral Reef! The Vanishing Undersea World	18
Ages: 8 & up	Dangerous Creatures	22
	Dinosaurs!	22
	Discoveries: Sky High	18
Ages: 8 & up	Dr. Health'nstein's Body Fun	17
Ages: 6-10	Explorapedia: The World of Nature	21

Kids/Science Continued…

	Exploring the Solar System and Beyond	13
Ages: 11 & up	How Animals Move	19
Ages: 12 & up	How Your Body Works	18
	In the Company of Whales	17
Ages: 12 & up	Isaac Asimov's The Ultimate Robot	15
	Journey to the Planets	10
Ages: 7 & up	Mammals: A Multimedia Encyclopedia	16
	New Dictionary of the Living World	20
Ages: 7 & up	Ocean Planet	15
Ages: 9 & up	Planetary Taxi	20
	Prehistoria: A Multimedia Who's Who of Prehistoric Life	15
	Safari	19
Ages: 8 & up	San Diego Zoo Presents ... The Animals! Version 2.0	21
Ages: 12 & up	Science Sleuths, Volume 1	20
Ages: 12 & up	Science Sleuths, Volume 2	19
Ages: 8 & up	Sharks!	17
Ages: 10 & up	Stephen Biesty's Incredible Cross-Sections Stowaway	21
Ages: 8 & up	Way Things Work	22
Ages: 5-11	Welcome to Bodyland	11
Ages: 8 & up	Widget Workshop	18
Ages: 5-9	Zurk's Rainforest Lab: Life Science and Math	15

KIDS/STORIES

Ages: 5-10	Alistair and the Alien Invasion	18
Ages: 6-10	Arthur's Birthday	20
Ages: 6-10	Arthur's Teacher Trouble	22
Ages: 3-10	Berenstain Bears Get in a Fight	20
Ages: 3-10	Big Anthony's Mixed-up Magic	17
Ages: 8-13	Black Beauty	17
	Casper Brainy Book	19
Ages: 3-6	Chugalong Goes to Playland	11
Ages: 6-12	Circus	20
Ages: 7 & up	Dazzeloids	15
Ages: 3-7	Dr. Seuss's ABC	23
Ages: 3-7	George Shrinks	15
Ages: 4-8	Get Ready For School, Charlie Brown!	–
Ages: 3-8	Harry and the Haunted House	21
Ages: 3-7	If You Give a Mouse a Cookie	16
	Indian in the Cupboard	–
Ages: 5-8	Jungle Book	16
Ages: 3-8	Just Grandma and Me	22

Subject Index

Age Range	Title	Overall Rating
Ages: 3-9	Lion King Animated Storybook	18
Ages: 3 & up	Little Monster at School	20
Ages: all	Manhole CD-ROM Masterpiece Edition	17
Ages: 4-10	My Favorite Monster	18
Ages: 6-10	Peter Pan	21
Ages: 5-7	Reader Rabbit's Reading Development Library, Level 1	22
Ages: 5-7	Reader Rabbit's Reading Development Library, Level 2	22
Ages: 3-8	Ruff's Bone	20
Ages: 5-8	Scooter's Magic Castle	19
Ages: 3-8	Tortoise and the Hare	23
Ages: 3-7	Winnie the Pooh and the Honey Tree	19
Ages: 3-8	World of Totty Pig	19

Kids/Stories & Poems

Ages: 3-8	Mixed-Up Mother Goose	18
Ages: 6-10	New Kid On The Block	22
Ages: 6-12	Somebody Catch My Homework	18

Language

	All-in-One Language Fun!	19
	American Sign Language Dictionary on CD-ROM	18
	Transparent Language Now! Series @	–

Language/English

	Rosetta Stone English, Level Ia	16
	TriplePlay Plus! English	18

Language/French

	Berlitz Think and Talk French	15
	French Now!	18
	Learn to Speak French, Version 4.0	20
	Rosetta Stone Francais, Level Ia	18
	TriplePlay Plus! French	17

Language/German

	Berlitz Think and Talk German	13
	German Now!	19
	TriplePlay Plus! German	18

Language/Italian

	Berlitz Think and Talk Italian	13
	Italian Now!	19

Language/Japanese

	Berlitz Live! Japanese	21
	Learn to Speak Japanese, Version 3.0	15
	Power Japanese	20

Language/Russian

	Rosetta Stone Russian, Level Ia	19

LANGUAGE/SPANISH

Berlitz Live! Spanish   20
Berlitz Think and Talk Spanish   15
Learn To Speak Spanish, Version 5.0   20
Power Spanish   16
Rosetta Stone Espanol, Level Ia   18
Spanish Now!   20
TriplePlay Plus! Spanish   19

LITERATURE

Complete Multimedia Bible   18
Discovering Shakespeare   17
Essential Frankenstein   16
Great Literature Plus   17
Macbeth   20
Poetry in Motion   19
Romeo & Juliet   17
Trouble Is My Business   13
Twain's World   14

LOGIC GAMES
     See Games/Puzzle & Logic

MAPS
     See Geography/Maps; see also Travel/Maps &
     Atlases

MATH
     See Kids/Edugames-Math

MEDICAL REFERENCE

A.D.A.M. The Inside Story   22
Bodyworks 4.0   18
Doctor's Book of Home Remedies   13
Dr. Scheuler Presents The Corner Drugstore –
Dr. Schueler's Home Medical
     Advisor Pro, Version 4.0   19
Dr. Schueler's Self Health   18
Mayo Clinic Family Health Book   16
Mayo Clinic Family Pharmacist   20
Mayo Clinic Sports Health & Fitness   15
Mayo Clinic: The Total Heart   17
Nine Month Miracle   19
Understanding Breast Cancer   12

MOVIES
Ages: 8-13   Black Beauty   17
Essential Frankenstein   16
Hard Day's Night   17
Macbeth   20
Romeo & Juliet   17
This is Spinal Tap   20

Movies/Reference

Blockbuster Video Guide to
Movies & Videos   14
Cinemania '95   21

Multi-Packs & Collections

3 Ft., 6 PAK For Kids   –
5 Ft. 10 PAK Special Edition 5 Ft. 10 PAK
Collectors Edition.   –
5 Ft., 10 PAK, Volume 1   –
5 Ft., 10 PAK, Volume 2   –
Composer Collection   20

Music/Appreciation

Ages: 3-8   Chuck Jones' Peter and the Wolf   18
Composer Collection   20
Grammys: 35 Years of Excellence in Music   16
Introduction to Classical Music   19
Jazz: A Multimedia History   13
Ages: 5-11   KidRiffs   16
Midisoft Multimedia Songbook   13
Midisoft Music Mentor Maestro Edition   14
Musical Instruments   23
Rock 'N' Roll Your Own   18
Ages: 5 & up   Stradiwackius: The Counting Concert   16
Xplora 1: Peter Gabriel's Secret World   17

Music/Interactive Albums

Bad Day on the Midway   –
Bob Dylan: Highway 61 Interactive   19
Freak Show   21
Gingerbread Man   18
Hard Day's Night   17
Headcandy   12
Jump: The David Bowie
Interactive CD-ROM   12
Meet MediaBand   17
Prince Interactive   17
Puppet Motel   19
This is Spinal Tap   20
Xplora 1: Peter Gabriel's Secret World   17

Music/Kids

Ages: 3-8   Chuck Jones' Peter and the Wolf   18
Ages: 3-9   CyberBoogie! with Sharon, Lois & Bram   14
Ages: 3-10   Dr. T's Sing-A-Long Around the World   20
Ages: 3-10   Dr. T's Sing-A-Long Kids Classics   17
Ages: 5-11   KidRiffs   16
Ages: 7 & up   Lenny's MusicToons   18
Midisoft Music Mentor Maestro Edition   14
Musical Instruments   23
Ages: 3 & up TuneLand   20

MYSTERY GAMES
    See Games/Mystery

PARLOR GAMES
    See Games/Parlor

PERSONAL DEVELOPMENT
            Create Your Dream Job   17
            Dr. Ruth's Encyclopedia of Sex   19
            It's Legal Deluxe   19
            Joy of Sex   11
            Men Are From Mars, Women
                Are From Venus   15
            Multimedia IQ Test   12
            Perfect Resume   16

PETS
            Dogs   13
            Kittens to Cats   16
            Multimedia Cats   19
            Multimedia Dogs 2.0   20

PHONE DIRECTORIES
            11 Million Businesses Phone Directory   15
            70 Million Households Phone Book   11
            800 Number Phone Book   14
            American White Pages, 1995 Edition   17
            American Yellow Pages, 1995 Edition   17
            Business Phone '96   18
            Canada Phone   18
            Direct Phone   20
            Free Phone   15
            Home & Business Phone '96   18
            Home Phone '96   19
            PhoneDisc '95 Business   18
            PhoneDisc '95 Business Lite   17
            PhoneDisc '95 Combo Pack   18
            PhoneDisc '95 Powerfinder   19
            PhoneDisc '95 Residential   18
            Pro CD Basic Information @   –
            Select Phone, 1996 Edition   19

PHOTOGRAPHY
            Better Photography: Learning to see
                Creatively   19
            From Alice to Ocean:
                Alone Across the Outback   19
            I Photograph to Remember   20
            Passage to Vietnam   23
            Understanding Exposure   17

POETRY
    See Literature; see also Kids/Stories & Poems

PUZZLE GAMES
    See Games/Puzzle & Logic

READING
    See Kids/Edugames - Reading

REFERENCE/ANTHOLOGY
            Bookshelf '95   23
            Discovering Shakespeare   17
            Essential Frankenstein   16
            Great Literature Plus   17
            Multimedia Business 500, Release 2   18
            Poetry in Motion   19
            Trouble Is My Business   13
            Twain's World   14
            World's Greatest Speeches   19

REFERENCE/DICTIONARIES
            American Heritage Talking Dictionary   20
            Bookshelf '95   23
Ages: 8-12 Merriam-Webster's Dictionary for Kids   18
Ages: 4-7   My First Incredible, Amazing Dictionary   21
            Random House Unabridged Dictionary,
                Second Edition   19

REFERENCE/ENCYCLOPEDIAS
            1995 Grolier Multimedia Encyclopedia   20
            1995 Guinness Multimedia Disc of Records   18
            Bookshelf '95   23
            Britannica CD   14
            Compton's Interactive Encyclopedia   19
            Encarta '95   22
Ages: 6-12 Heinemann Children's Multimedia
                Encyclopedia   12
Ages: 11 & up InfoPedia   11
Ages: 3-6   My First Encyclopedia   19
Ages: 11 & up Webster's Interactive Encyclopedia   10

REFERENCE/KIDS
            1995 Grolier Multimedia Encyclopedia   20
            Britannica CD   14
            Compton's Interactive Encyclopedia   19
            Encarta '95   22
Ages: 6-10 Explorapedia: The World of Nature   21
Ages: 6-10 Explorapedia: The World of People   19
Ages: 6-12 Heinemann Children's Multimedia
                Encyclopedia   12
Ages: 11 & up InfoPedia   11
Ages: 8-12 Merriam-Webster's Dictionary for Kids   18
Ages: 3-6   My First Encyclopedia   19
Ages: 4-7   My First Incredible, Amazing Dictionary   21

Reference/Kids Continued…
Ages: all   Rand McNally's Children's Atlas
                    of the United States   17
Ages: 11 & up Webster's Interactive Encyclopedia   10

REFERENCE/SPORTS
        See Sports/Reference

RELATIONSHIPS
                Dr. Ruth's Encyclopedia of Sex   19
                Joy of Sex   11
                Men Are From Mars,
                    Women Are From Venus   15

RELIGION
                Beyond the Sambatyon:
                    The Myth of the Ten Lost Tribes   18
                Complete Multimedia Bible   18

ROLE-PLAYING GAMES
        See Games /Role Playing & Interactive Fiction

SCIENCE/ANATOMY
Ages: 7 & up 3-D Body Adventure   19
                A.D.A.M. The Inside Story   22
Ages: 8 & up AnnaTommy: An Adventure into
                    the Human Body   11
Ages: 4-10   Body Park   14
                Bodyworks 4.0   18
                Doctor's Book of Home Remedies   13
Ages: 8 & up Dr. Health'nstein's Body Fun   17
                Dr. Ruth's Encyclopedia of Sex   19
                Dr. Scheuler Presents The Corner Drugstore   –
                Dr. Schueler's Home Medical Advisor Pro,
                    Version 4.0   19
                Dr. Schueler's Self Health   18
Ages: 12 & up How Your Body Works   18
Ages: 6-10   Magic School Bus Explores the
                    Human Body   19
                Mayo Clinic: The Total Heart   17
                Nine Month Miracle   19
                Ultimate Human Body   20
                Understanding Breast Cancer   12
Ages: 5-11   Welcome to Bodyland   11

SCIENCE/ANIMALS
                Antarctica   16
Ages: 6 & up Coral Reef! The Vanishing Undersea World   18
Ages: 8 & up Dangerous Creatures   22
                Dogs   13
Ages: 6-10   Explorapedia: The World of Nature   21
Ages: 11 & up How Animals Move   19

	In the Company of Whales	17
	Kittens to Cats	16
Ages: 7 & up	Mammals: A Multimedia Encyclopedia	16
	Multimedia Cats	19
	Multimedia Dogs 2.0	20
	New Dictionary of the Living World	20
	OceanLife, Volume 4:	
	The Great Barrier Reef	18
Ages: 4 & up	Professor Iris' Fun Field Trip:	
	Animal Safari	12
	Safari	19
Ages: 8 & up	San Diego Zoo Presents ...	
	The Animals! Version 2.0	21
Ages: 8 & up	Sharks!	17
Ages: 5-12	Undersea Adventure	18
	Wolf	16
Ages: 5-9	Zurk's Rainforest Lab: Life Science	
	and Math	15

SCIENCE/ASTRONOMY

Ages: 9-17	Astronomica: The Quest for the Edge	
	of the Universe	15
Ages: 13 & up	Buzz Aldrin's Race Into Space	10
Ages: 14 & up	Distant Suns: Desktop Planetarium	17
	Exploring the Solar System and Beyond	13
	Journey to the Planets	10
Ages: 6-10	Magic School Bus Explores the	
	Solar System	20
Ages: 9 & up	Planetary Taxi	20
Ages: 11 & up	RedShift	21
Ages: 14 & up	Stephen Hawking's A Brief History	
	of Time	17

SCIENCE/DINOSAURS

Ages: 3 & up

	3-D Dinosaur Adventure	15
	Dinosaurs!	22
	Prehistoria: A Multimedia Who's Who of	
	Prehistoric Life	15

SCIENCE - KIDS

    See Kids/Edugames - Science; see also
    Kids/Science

SCIENCE/GENERAL

	Antarctica	16
	Big Green Disc	13
Ages: 3-8	Bug Adventure	19
Ages: 6 & up	Coral Reef! The Vanishing Undersea World	18
	Discoveries: Sky High	18
	Earthquake	14

SUBJECT INDEX

Age Range	Title	Overall Rating

Science/General Continued...

	Eyewitness Encyclopedia of Science	17
	Jets!	17
	Leonardo the Inventor	16
Ages: 7 & up	Ocean Planet	15
	OceanLife, Volume 4: The Great Barrier Reef	18
Ages: 8 & up	Sharks!	17
Ages: 14 & up	Stephen Hawking's A Brief History of Time	17
	Warplanes: Modern Flying Aircraft	18
Ages: 8 & up	Way Things Work	22
	Wild Blue Yonder, Episode 1: 50 Years of Gs and Jets	18
Ages: 5-9	Zurk's Rainforest Lab: Life Science and Math	15

SIMULATION GAMES
    See Games/Simulation

SOCIAL STUDIES
    See Kids/Edugames - Social Studies

SPELLING
    See Kids/Edugames - Spelling

SPORTS/INSTRUCTIONAL
    See Sports/Reference

SPORTS/REFERENCE

	75 Seasons: The History of the NFL	21
	Baseball's Greatest Hits	19
	Bill James Electronic Baseball Encyclopedia	18
	Complete Baseball '95	21
	Complete NBA Basketball	20
	ESPN Interactive Golf: Lower Your Score with Tom Kite – Shot Making	17
	ESPN Interactive Golf: Lower Your Score with Tom Kite – The Full Swing and Putting	17
Ages: 12 & up	ESPN Let's Play Tennis	14
	Everything You Want to Know About Sports Encyclopedia	19
	Extreme Sports	19
	FIFA International Soccer	19
	Fly Fishing: Great Rivers of the West	22
	Martial Arts Explorer	16
	Michigan and Notre Dame Football	20
	Mountain Biking	17
	Skier's Encyclopedia	12
	Sports Illustrated Multimedia Almanac, 1995 Edition	19

SUBJECT INDEX		
Age Range	Title	Overall Rating

Ages: 12 & up Warren Miller's Ski World — 20

SPORTS SIMULATION GAMES
    See Games/Sports Simulation

STORIES
    See Kids/Stories

TEST PREPARATION

Cliffs Studyware for the S.A.T. I	11
Your Personal Trainer for the SAT, Version 2.0	21

TRAVEL

Everywhere USA Travel Guide	15
Expert Travel Planner	14
Great Restaurants, Wineries & Breweries	12
Let's Go: Budget Guide to Europe	15
Taxi	21

TRAVEL/MAPS & ATLASES

AAA Trip Planner	14
Automap Road Atlas	19
Everywhere USA Travel Guide	15
Expert Travel Planner	14
Map 'n' Go	18
MapExpert 2.0	18
Rand McNally's Tripmaker	19
Street Atlas USA 2.0	20
Taxi	21

TYPING

Ages: 5 & up	Mario Teaches Typing	18
Ages: 9 & up	Mavis Beacon Teaches Typing for Kids	14
	Mavis Beacon Teaches Typing, Version 3.0	22
	Multimedia Typing Instructor	19

WAR
    See History/War

WINE, BEER & SPIRITS

Beer Homebrewing Guide	15
Beer Hunter	17
Food & Wine's Wine Tasting: An Interactive Experience	16
Great Restaurants, Wineries & Breweries	12
Wine Guide	24
Wines of the World	16

WRITING TOOLS FOR KIDS
    See Kids/Art & Writing

United **CD ROM**

Dear CD-ROM Enthusiast,

As you search for the best in multimedia entertainment and productivity, please call us at 1-800-UNITED4. United CD-ROM has over 2,500 multimedia products in stock everyday for same day shipping. We have access to another 10,000 within 48 hours. Contact us at:

Phone:	1-800-864-8334
Fax:	1-217-352-9749
BBS	217-352-9654
America On-Line	Member Name: UNITEDCD
Compuserve	76043.1605

Call for a Free Catalog!

We have the best prices on the largest selection. Contact us today.

HUGE SELECTION! CALL FOR MORE DETAILS AND MORE TITLES! MAC AND WINDOW PRODUCTS!

Edutainment

40854	Circle of Knowledge
44195	Fun to Learn Bundles
38890	Math Blaster
41671	Putt-Putt Goes to the Moon
43608	Where in the World is Carmen SanDiego?

Games

34920	Star Trek: Final Unity
40565	Apache
34615	Myst
40203	Wing Commander 3
42222	Journeyman 2

Education

36995	Incredible Machine 2
40276	Interactive Space Encyclopedia
43882	Typing Teacher
31580	Mario Teaches Typing
42593	Triple Play Plus Spanish

For Kids

36294	Winnie the Pooh Storybook
36300	Aladdin Activity Center
36280	Lion King Storybook
36382	The Way Things Work
36383	My First Dictionary

Productivity

39383	Quicken 4 Deluxe
41788	Four Paws of the Crab Cookbook
38514	Home Medical Advisor
43011	Home Repair Encyclopedia
44139	Compton's Interactive Encyclopedia

Other Titles

44432	Linux 4 CD Set
43636	QRZ Home Radio
35112	Clip Art Heaven 2
42836	Font Fascination
44049	Supra Express 14.4 Fax Modem

1-800-864-8334

The Edutainment Catalog

1-800-338-3844

Hundreds of CD-ROM Titles
Discount Prices
30 Day Guarantee
Free Technical Support

The 48 page Edutainment Catalog is a great source of CD-ROM software for your family's computer. We offer a wide selection for kids, as well as numerous entertainment, reference, education, and leisure titles for adults. All the major publishers are well represented in the catalog, and you won't find any violent games or sexually oriented programs. Our prices are very competitive, and we offer a 30-day guarantee in case you have hardware compatibility problems or the program just wasn't what you expected. Our catalog is also available on CD-ROM and on the Internet World Wide Web at WWW.edutainco.com. For more information call 800-338-3844 or 303-444-3700.

YOU'LL FIND THE
BEST-SELLING TITLES FROM:

Broderbund • The Learning Company • Microsoft • Davidson • Disney Software • The Discovery Channel • Edmark • Sierra Knowledge Adventure • IBM • MECC • Dorling Kindersley • National Geographic • Grolier • any many more!!